WILDERNESS STRANGERS

WILDERNESS STRANGERS

Adventures in Shangri-La

J.C. Mitchell

LUMINARE PRESS
WWW.LUMINAREPRESS.COM

AUTHOR'S NOTE

This book describes the author's experiences during the 1950s, '60s, '70s, and '80s and reflects his opinions relating to those experiences.

Names, descriptions, and details of individuals identified in this book have been changed to protect their privacy. Any resemblance to other people, events, places, or situations is strictly coincidental.

Wilderness Strangers: Adventures in Shangri-La

Printed in the United States of America

Luminare Press
442 Charnelton St.
Eugene, OR 97401
www.luminarepress.com

LCCN: 2022914417
ISBN: 979-8-88679-046-7

For Keldon Tjaden, Mary Kay Swanson
and Ralph Cameron Mitchell
with all my love

Contents

Acknowledgments

An entire universe of like-minded wilderness aficionados, including trail dogs, freelance adventurers, and dirtbag climbers, contributed to this book.

First and foremost, a special tip of the hardhat to Doug Baldwin for his content suggestions, editing acumen, and keen insights and witticisms related to life as a trail dog and wilderness ranger for the US Forest Service.

Many thanks to Paul Sharaba and Rick Newman for their editing and content suggestions in helping create this memoir. Also, major thanks to Kathy Kifer, graphic designer/illustrator extraordinaire, who created the cover for this book, and to KC Crowley for his map illustration of the Lake Wenatchee Ranger District.

I would also like to acknowledge many others who helped with my research and development for *Wilderness Strangers*, including Mary Kay Swanson, Mick Tjaden, Chuck Ferguson, Frank Stevens, Craig McKern, Heather Murphy, Byron Newell, Corky Broaddus, Connie Cook, Bob Ness, Kevin Pedersen, Frank Czubiak, Alyson Pytte, Roger Ross, Steve Steinke, Michael Sweeney, Roger Wallace, Tom Wilkinson, Glen Sims, Lee Rosin, and Galen Tritt.

Finally, thanks to my family: Rebecca, Gina, and Jory, who watched me write, rewrite, edit, proofread, edit, and rewrite ad nauseam on this book.

J.C.M.

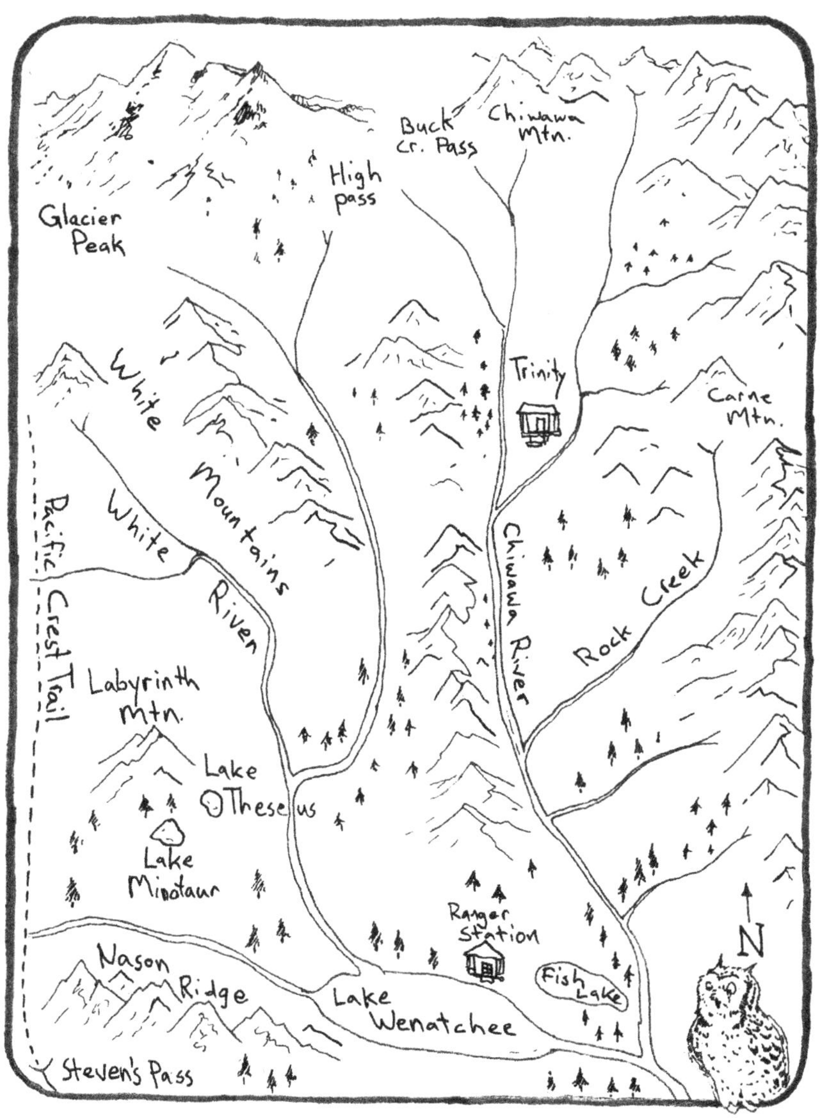

Map of Lake Wenatchee Ranger District by KC Crowley

CHAPTER ONE
Lone Wolf

He was from a large family, but he wouldn't have known it—at least initially. Kieran "Kerry" Jon Weiss was a surprise. His parents, Albert George and Lois Hannah Weiss, were in their mid-fifties when Kerry was born in Dickinson, North Dakota. His four older siblings had already left the family home. Some were married and starting families of their own. Kerry was essentially an only child.

The town of Dickinson, with about eight thousand residents when Kerry entered the world, is located in the Northern Great Plains, closer to Moose Jaw, Saskatchewan, than to Bozeman, Montana. His dad worked at a local car dealership and his mom, initially a teacher, was a homemaker. Al fancied himself a poet and penned this sonnet on the birth of his second son:

Twill soon be time to announce
New automobiles for '53.
Like Cadillac—Chevrolet and Olds—
By the Sax Motor Company.
Now these are all top productions,
The finest built in USA,
But I, Al Weiss, Parts Manager,
Announce a model of my own today.
This model has been delivered
By Dr. Rodgers, our family MD,
And for your own information

He's on display at St. Joseph's Nursery.
He arrived November 22
Via the famous old stork line.
And I'm happy to tell you that
He and his mom are doing fine.
We couldn't name him
Cadillac, Olds, or Chevrolet.
Instead, we call him Kieran Jon,
We decided that today.
He tips the gauge on scale
To 7 pounds, 1.5 ounces at par.
Drop in to see us sometime
And have a cigar.

Almost immediately, his parents recognized that Kerry was a quick learner. He knew the words and tune of "Sing a Song of Sixpence" before he could fully talk. As a young man, he was athletic. But at age twelve he contracted mononucleosis, so instead of trying out for a team sport, Kerry entered a reading contest. He was so good at reading that he won the contest. Reading would become a lifestyle for Kerry, setting him off on a path to knowledge and education.

Rather than competing in track or football, young Kerry took up archery. He became a skilled marksman and won the state junior archery championship. Soon, he developed into an avid hunter in the hills and dales of North Dakota and Montana.

Dickinson is known as the gateway to Theodore Roosevelt National Park and its bounty of recreational opportunities, including hiking, climbing, and exploring—activities that Kerry would eagerly embrace, mostly by himself. In many ways, he was becoming a lone wolf.

In late 1971, Kerry received a low number in the draft lottery that began in 1969 to supply manpower for the war in Vietnam. Kerry landed at Fort Leonard Wood on January 3, 1972. There he met Lee Roberts at about four o'clock in the morning on January 4, when their drill sergeant wandered down the aisle of their wooden WWII-era barracks, banging on a garbage can cover and screaming at the top of his lungs.

Lee was in a top bunk, and as he sat up, he found Kerry's eyes directly across the aisle from him as they said in unison, "What the fuck are we doing here?"

"We spent the two months of basic training humoring each other with the absurdity of all things military," said Lee.

At that time, the counterculture had seeped into the brains of the two small-town kids from the frozen Upper Midwest.

"Kerry had a cassette player, so he introduced me to *Welcome to the Canteen* and the deep cuts on *Layla, and Other Assorted Love Songs*," said Lee. "I insisted that he listen more carefully to King Crimson and Jethro Tull, and we agreed on the transformative effects of Crosby, Stills, Nash & Young and the British Invasion."

The newfound friends irritated the hell out of the military types during those months, but the US had yet to move to an all-volunteer army, so their superiors had little recourse for their antics. When a lens fell out of his glasses and broke, Kerry put a patch of masking tape over the frame, sketched a very nice peace sign on it, and spent several weeks pissing off everyone he had to salute.

"We would stand in formation at mail call, waiting for news and goodies from home," said Lee, "and our drill sergeant would target us for his social commentary. 'Package for Weiss.' 'Package for Roberts.' 'Another load of dope!'"

In hindsight, Kerry and Lee survived those two months with ease. Both were good athletes, so the physical part was no problem.

"Kerry was an interesting case because, not being a team sports guy, he was kind of a sleeper," recalled Lee. "He was stronger than most but didn't exactly look like it. He did, however, have tremendous stamina. His days hunting in the Turtle Mountains of North Dakota had its effect. I remember when we had to do a timed two-mile run in fatigues and army boots. Kerry smoked just about everybody, including some track stars."

The pair parted ways after they completed basic training. "Kerry was destined for Fort Gordon in Georgia for Military Police training," Lee added.

But his MP role was derailed by a bag of weed discovered in his footlocker as he was about to finish basic training. Incredibly, the incident turned into a good break because his superiors weren't sure what to do with him.

So, Kerry was sent to Germany and assigned as a courier. His job was to deliver messages to colonels and generals at various US military installations in Southern Germany. He rode trains all over Europe for about eighteen months, learned to drink excellent beer, and discovered the Alps.

Kerry would write to document his European adventures and read books by Hunter S. Thompson, Edward Abbey, Aldo Leopold, and Ernest Hemingway. He would come to believe that the general state of the world was now currently fucked up.

At the American base in Stuttgart, Germany, at Seventh Corps Headquarters, Kerry met a fellow soldier who would become his lifelong pal, Sam Schmidt, an army photographer who hailed from Atlanta, Georgia. Together, they made it their mission to wage war on the army for having the gall to draft them.

"Our shared philosophy was that 'it's us against the army,'" Schmidt recalled.

Kerry also met and dated a red-headed woman, a civilian who lived and worked at the army base, Teresa Marie O'Flanigan from Seattle, Washington.

"I'll be heading back to the Seattle area soon," she told Kerry. "You should join me when you're discharged."

"Sounds good," assured Kerry. "I sure as hell ain't going back to Dickinson."

Honorably discharged by the army after a mere eighteen months of service, Kerry flew back to North Dakota, packed up his belongings, and drove to the Pacific Northwest. His relationship with Teresa didn't last long, but Kerry had become hooked on Seattle.

Soon, Sam Schmidt loaded his Dodge van in Atlanta and joined Kerry, where he was now living with his new girlfriend, Shannon Wilson, and her mother, Ginny, on Queen Anne Hill. Kerry became a Seattleite, cheering the home team, the University of Washington Huskies. Often, Kerry would pack Shannon's yellow VW camper bus for a road trip, and they would then jump the ferry to Bainbridge Island to partake of salmon, blackberry pie, and a hot tub.

One of their favorite trips took Kerry and Shannon over Snoqualmie Pass to Cle Elum, an old mining community located near the Teanaway River Road toward the Ingalls Lake Trailhead. Kerry always planned and directed their excursions, as was his style.

This time, his plan for the couple was to hike over the pass to Ingalls Lake, then scale the shoulder of Mt. Stuart, and drop into the Icicle River trail toward Leavenworth. But about a hundred yards up the trail, it was clear that his grand plans would never materialize. Shannon was barely hanging in there, while Kerry ran up the switchbacks with a stuffed pack, much like a mountain goat.

Crying ensued, and Kerry eventually determined that he would need to amend his plans. He ran down from the ridgetop and carried Shannon's pack up the trail, deciding instead to camp at Ingalls Lake for a couple of nights, pursue easier day hikes, then retreat to the Ingalls Lake Trailhead.

Life was good as Kerry lived with Shannon in their beloved Seattle. They made many trips to the Pike Place Market to purchase ingredients for feasts at Ginny's. Kerry and Shannon would spend a few days in the Olympics, camping on the beach at La Push. Shannon and Kelly were inevitable yet imperfect together: two bright and strong-willed persons, both fantastically independent.

When the time came for Kerry to decide on a college, he settled on Central Washington University in Ellensburg, Washington, to pursue a degree in environmental studies. Kerry and Shannon subsequently moved to the university neighborhood in Ellensburg.

There, the pair met Richard Oldman, also known as "El Reeko," a good friend with whom Kerry would climb Mt. Stuart. Later, Rick, Kerry, and Shannon would scuba dive near Deception Pass on Whidbey Island.

Together, Kerry and Shannon would paddle the waters of Puget Sound and ski in the North Cascades. Snow camping together, they could spend a whole morning watching a heavy snowfall while huddled around a warm fire, followed by miles and miles of trekking to the squeaky tune of waxed skis on fresh powder, or "pow," as Kerry liked to call it.

After a year, Kerry decided that he was at the wrong university for the type of degree he needed to pursue, so he transferred to Western Washington University's Huxley College of the Environment in Bellingham to study urban planning and community affairs. Kerry took the planning discipline seriously. Aside from school, his only interest, besides Shannon, was exploring the outdoors, hiking, and kayaking from his home on Lake Sammamish.

Shortly after their move to Bellingham to pursue a degree in urban planning, Shannon was diagnosed with a brain tumor, which proved to be inoperable. From there, she deteriorated rapidly and was placed under hospice care at her mother's home on Queen Anne Hill. Kerry hastily crafted a letter to Rick to provide an update:

Dear Rick:

Two things today so far to report: the hospice nurse, Mary, who is a wonderful person, visited this morning to examine Shannon. Hospice nurses visit two-to-three times a week or as needed. Hospice care only started Monday, so this was Mary's first visit since the initial intake assessment. Shannon appears to be well on her way and may die very soon. She is entering the transition.

Last night, Shannon said, 'No more visitors.' She is breathing on her own now and is resting comfortably. Mary is doing a phenomenal job of handling her medications for her. The meds are now only for her comfort—morphine and a solution to keep fluids from accumulating in the back of her throat.

After Mary left, I went out for breakfast and her friends Carol, Holly, Vicki, Rene, and Susan sat with Shannon and held hands. Shannon was able to reach out to hug Holly. Even though she is not lucid and opening her eyes, Shannon acknowledged everyone and began breathing easier. They all breathed together.

Her friend Susan has been working with Shannon ever since she was diagnosed in terms of moving through the process. Susan is also a hospice volunteer as well as a dear friend of Shannon, who seems to be acknowledging and appreciating all the love being offered. Often, when close to death, people are off in their own world and don't seem to acknowledge others as they are already on their final journey in life. So, this was key for her friends. Another gift from Shannon.

We are all enjoying each other's company a lot, catching up on our history together. We are having so many laughs about Ginny and Shannon and our relationships and experiences with them. Thank you for your concern and support; this house is rich with good spirit. Thank you, Rick, for the opportunity to reach out to you and write my way through this.

Love, Kerry

About two weeks after her diagnosis, Shannon died. Before she was diagnosed with cancer, Shannon knew what she wanted for her final resting place. She had envisioned Kerry spreading her ashes on an outgoing tide from Deception Pass on the north end of Whidbey Island to the strains of "Stairway to Heaven" by Led Zeppelin.

After Shannon's memorial service, Kerry sent another letter to Rick Oldman.

Dear Rick:

On Saturday, August 29th, about twenty-five people gathered to celebrate and release Shannon's ashes to the waters of Puget Sound. The day couldn't have been any more beautiful. From our picnic site, we looked out over the metallic sheen of the water to a couple of islands dotting the landscape beyond the Olympic Mountains and above, the azure blue sky. People brought their pictures, music, stories, food, and open hearts.

In groups big and small, memories were relived, folks were reacquainted, tears and hugs abounded, and laughter rang out. Dictated by the tides, at around four o'clock in the afternoon, we all took a short hike to a picture-perfect cove to fulfill Shannon's wish.

Along the way, we saw an eagle soaring overhead and knew Shannon was with us. Atop a large rock that sat at the sea's edge, a spontaneous memorial touched my heart. Driftwood, rocks, shells, and feathers were beautifully placed along with a candle for remembrance. A cassette recorder played a selection of Shannon's favorite tunes.

Three kayaks waited on shore and the first to go out to sea was good old Charlie, a long-time cat of Shannon's who had been cremated years before. Samson, another of Shannon's cats, was next, ready to join his buddy, Charlie. Again, the kayaks glided out to the current to let him go.

Finally, it was time to let our Shannon go. I turned off the music and some people spoke—we heard how long it would take her ashes to circle the world and recalled how she loved traveling. We heard that she would return to earth again in the form of rain and we all smiled at the thought of how much she hated rain. People then said their good-byes in whispers and aloud and we all held each other a little closer.

As the kayaks, so smooth in the water, left the shore, "Stairway to Heaven" was playing. Once out in the currents, I swung my raised arms. As Shannon was released, hoots and hollers were heard along with heartfelt cries and Led Zeppelin blasted through the speakers. It was perfect!

When the kayaks returned, some folks dove in the water, and toasts were offered until we ran out of wine. Not to worry though, there was more back at the picnic site, where more hugs abounded, and more tears shed. Right then, I realized the release wasn't just for Shannon's ashes. The experience was a release for each of us.

We lingered a bit at the cove with folks slowly making their way home. Carol and I, among the last to leave, spotted that eagle again circling overhead and agreed: "Yeah, we did Shannon good." We saw the beautiful raptor light on a tree, and when we passed under it again, we gave Shannon our thanks.

Back at the picnic site, more food and stories were shared. The sunset held us in awe and the bonfire was lit. I thought it would be a place to burn my letters and cards that Shannon had saved over the years.

I opened one at random and read it aloud. It was a Conan the Barbarian story that had us laughing. Another letter and more laughs, and finally, I said: "I will keep these letters after all. I need to reread them."

As darkness descended and people left, the stars came out. Someone sitting by the fire told a Shannon story. I looked out at the night sky, saw a shooting star, and nodded my head to her as she once again filled my heart.

Eventually, the ranger came by and told the six or so of us remaining that it was time to go. We gathered our stuff, loaded the cars, and went back to the campfire to say goodbye. Shannon is forever in our hearts. For that we are grateful.

Love, Kerry

A month after Shannon's wake, Kerry remained devastated. He slowly settled into a yearlong period of depression and remorse.

CHAPTER TWO

Mountain Refugee

Like Kerry, Joseph Carl Blanco came from a family of five. Unlike Kerry, Joe was the oldest in the group of siblings. Born in Portland, Oregon, Joe lived in the Eastmoreland District and attended Catholic schools through twelfth grade. An urbanite from his youth, Joe nonetheless longed for the mountains, and he started climbing as a youngster in the Cascades of Oregon and Washington.

His dad, Paul Blanco, was an Italian immigrant who came to America before WWII to escape the fascist dictatorship of Benito Mussolini. A miner in the foothills of the Alps near Chialamberto in the Piedmont Region, Paul had led caravans through the mountains as a youth and was a skilled mountaineer.

When Paul arrived in Portland and enrolled in teachers college, he also joined two climbing clubs, the Mazamas based in Portland, and the Mountaineers based in Seattle, and he became an active participant in many of the group excursions.

When Joe was old enough, he joined his father, climbing Mt. Hood with a group of Mazamas at the age of eleven. Right near the Hogsback, at about the ten-thousand-foot level of the mountain near the summit, the lack of oxygen slowed young Joe's progress to a crawl. He was frustrated because he couldn't bound up the mountain as he did on many of the trails he had hiked as a Boy Scout.

His dad patiently explained the effects of altitude sickness on human physiology. "Take your time," he said encouragingly, "and we'll make it to the summit. You can do it, boy."

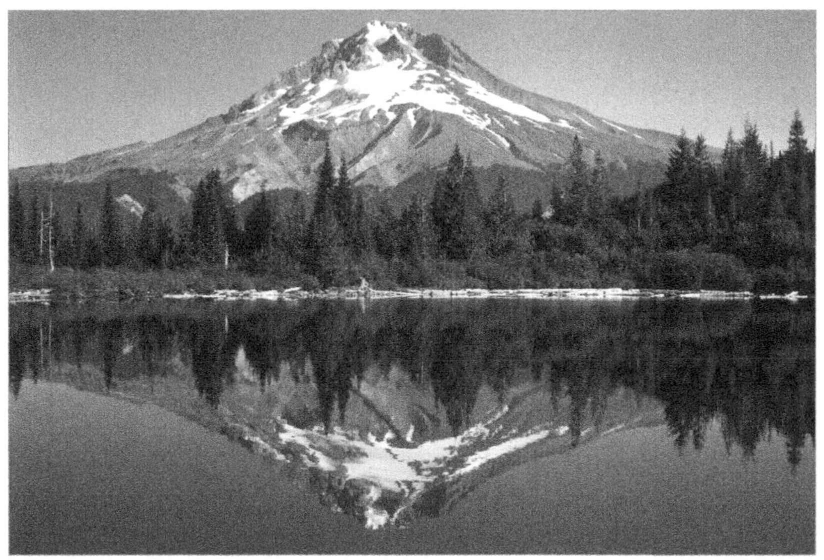

Mt. Hood reflected in Mirror Lake

After a good long break at the Hogsback, Joe was rejuvenated and ready to make the last push to the summit. Exhilarated at the apex of Oregon's tallest peak, he gazed out over the Columbia River below to the peaks to the north—Mt. St. Helens, Mt. Rainier, and Mt. Adams—and basked in his accomplishment.

"Dad, what have you learned from climbing all these years?" Joe asked.

"The pure simplicity of climbing clears your mind," his father responded. "When you're climbing, you can really focus. You lose all the distractions and confusion of life in Portland. The light up here is richer, the colors more vivid, and the sounds are sharper. Climbing requires the kind of focus that clears your mind."

Joe liked the sound of that. He was sold on climbing.

Soon, Joe was reading about the climbing exploits of all the great mountaineers of the Pacific Northwest, California, and around the world: Royal Robbins, Reinhold Messner, Jim and Lou Whittaker, and particularly Fred Beckey, Joe's favorite local climber. Like Beckey, Joe longed to be a freelance "dirtbag" climber.

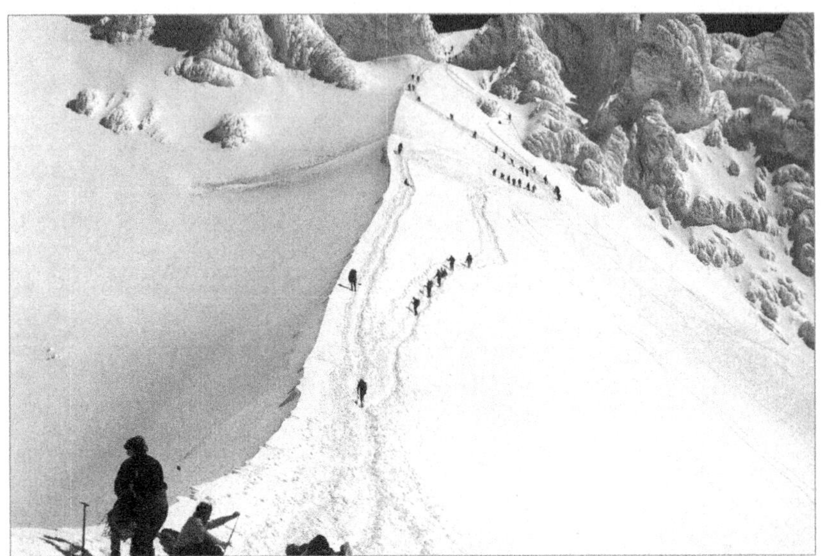

The Hogsback on Mt. Hood

While Joe enjoyed climbing with the Mazamas and his dad, he longed to hike and climb more with people his own age. As a Boy Scout, Joe hiked the trails and climbed many of the smaller peaks in Oregon. The troop took summer excursions, such as a fifty-mile trek from Timberline Lodge on Mt. Hood to the Columbia River Gorge at Eagle Creek. His troop also hiked the Obsidian Trail, from near McKenzie Pass around the west side of North Sister and Middle Sister to Green Lake at the base of South Sister, where Joe climbed solo to the summit.

As a college student at the University of Oregon, he went hiking and climbing on weekends in the central Cascades, summiting Diamond Peak, Middle Sister, and the Husband, along with smaller peaks like Scott Mountain and Black Crater.

When it came to his schooling, Joe's strong suit was English grammar, composition, and literature. He felt the writer's urge and worked on his grade school and high school newspapers, mostly covering sports. Once he graduated from high school in Portland, he ventured south to study journalism in Eugene.

With some experience as a fledgling journalist, Joe figured the next logical step would be to work as a reporter for the *Oregon Daily Emerald* (ODE), the student newspaper on campus. The paper had recently gained its independence from the University of Oregon in 1971 after a long legal struggle.

Originally under the auspices of the School of Journalism, the ODE was housed in Allen Hall. But now, times were changing in this country, with rallies, demonstrations, and even bombings on campus. Under the circumstances, university administrators attempted to clamp down on student protests and dictate the coverage of these demonstrations.

That's when visionary student journalists had decided otherwise: that the newspaper needed independence to safeguard its free, honest, and forthright student voice. The student paper won its lawsuit in court to become an independent publication and moved out of Allen Hall into the Erb Memorial Union, the student hub on campus.

Joe applied for a position as a reporter and was interviewed by editor-in-chief Dennis O'Meara.

O'Meara began, "I see from your resumé that you have experience working on your high school newspaper. Which beats did you cover?"

"Mostly sports," replied Joe.

"We have that department fully staffed right now," O'Meara responded. "Do you have any other areas of interest?"

"Yes," Joe said. "My minor is environmental sciences, and I'm interested in issues relating to the natural world. I have a particular story idea in mind concerning environmental misdeeds at Crater Lake National Park, where I worked last summer."

"We do need an environmental reporter," offered O'Meara, "and with Earth Day coming up, we'll need someone to cover all the stories relating to the increasing concern about our natural environment."

The ODE editor subsequently assigned Joe to the associate editor in charge of covering environmental issues. He wrote stories on land use planning, nuclear power, toxic waste disposal, cedar thievery on national forest land, and more.

Joe's story on Crater Lake was so well received that they featured the piece on the front page of their Friday edition, the largest circulation paper of the week. O'Meara suggested that Joe enter the story in the William Randolph Hearst Journalism Awards competition.

O'Meara encouraged him. "The story is that good," he said.

Despite the increasing pressure of his journalism classes and *Emerald* deadlines, Joe found the time to put together the application form for the awards program and submitted the story to the Hearst Foundation. Two weeks later, Joe learned that he had received an honorable mention in the Explanatory Writing category, which netted him $250. It appeared that a career in journalism was becoming a reality.

As the school year ended, Joe fished around for summer jobs. After a season of working for the concessionaire at Crater Lake as a tour guide and boat operator, he applied for a wilderness ranger position with the US Forest Service and was subsequently hired by the Malheur National Forest near John Day, Oregon.

In early June, the Malheur National Forest staff sent Joe, and the other Strawberry Mountain Wilderness ranger, Marcia Phelps to a training session in Bend, Oregon, joining other summer employees from around Oregon.

The group of seasonal US Forest Service employees resembled a collection of freelance mountaineers, dirtbag climbers, and college-age hippies, yet this cadre of apparent misfits represented the cream of wilderness rangers in the Northwest at that time.

Typically, many backcountry rangers were college students or recent graduates taking time off before entering the "real world." Some would patrol the woods for a few years and then move on to other careers. Some would eventually secure permanent positions with the USFS. The backgrounds of this group of rangers varied far and wide in terms of major areas of study. Subject areas ranged from forestry, geology, and computer science to journalism, philosophy, photography, and more.

On the trail to the summit of Strawberry Mountain

In the backcountry, wilderness rangers were on call twenty-four hours a day, often for seven-to-ten days at a time as medics, law enforcement officers, search-and-rescue specialists, and wilderness hosts. On good days, they might be asked to clean a campsite, find lost backpackers, or even save a hiker's life. On bad days, they might have to recover bodies.

On most typical days, however, they picked up trash, installed new directional signage, and dismantled illegal campfires and hunter camps. The training session focused on educating wilderness rangers on the variety of tasks they would be obliged to perform.

Back on the Malheur, Joe and Marcia patrolled their portions of the Strawberry Mountain Wilderness on the north side and south side, respectively. On rare occasions when they would meet in the wilderness, they would enjoy each other's company. Eventually, a romance blossomed, and soon they started spending their days and nights together in their off-hours.

Together, they particularly enjoyed climbing. Since the Strawberry Mountain Wilderness was smaller than other wilderness areas in Oregon, Joe and Marcia would meet to summit Strawberry Mountain, Rabbit Ears, Indian Creek Butte, Graham Mountain, Elk Mountain, Green Mountain, Sheep Rock, and Canyon Mountain.

One day, after climbing Canyon Mountain, the two wilderness rangers decided to stop in Seneca, Oregon, at the infamous Bear Valley Tavern. Basically a wide spot on the highway between John Day and Burns, Seneca was established in 1895. The town was named after a prominent Portland judge, Seneca Smith.

At the trailhead to Canyon Mountain, Marcia asked Joe, "Shall we check out the Bear Valley Tavern? It's on our way back to the ranger station."

"Sure, I'm game," came Joe's reply. "I could use a beer. Especially right now."

Historically, Bear Valley was first settled by the indigenous Northern Paiute tribes, followed by early homesteaders and trappers. The town, located in Bear Valley, would grow when it became the northern terminus of the now-defunct Oregon and Northwestern Railroad owned by the Edward Hines Lumber Company of Burns. The company had earlier initiated large-scale shipping of ponderosa pine logs to Burns for milling.

By the 1970s, however, logging began to decline, and the Hines Lumber Company ceased operations in the area. As a result, the population of Seneca dramatically diminished. According to the 1970 census, the town's population hovered at about two hundred residents. At that point, Seneca featured only a post office, a single grocery store, and one saloon.

The town's primary industries now were cattle ranching and some minor timber production. Seneca had the distinction of having recorded the lowest temperature ever in Oregon at fifty-four degrees below zero. The town, like most others in Grant County, was a haven for cowboys and loggers. Nothing illustrated the demographic social culture of the area better than the Bear Valley Tavern.

As they entered the saloon, the two uniformed wilderness guards immediately sensed that all eyes were on them, like strangers in a strange land. Sawdust covered the floor throughout the saloon, which featured an old-style bar with copper railing at the foot and tall, tattered bar stools. They tried not to visually react to a sign placed prominently behind the bar that read: "We reserve the right to kill anyone."

Joe and Marcia had heard about the Bear Valley Tavern from some of the permanent Forest Service employees in Prairie City.

"The Bear Valley Tavern in Seneca is one of most lowdown, dirty taverns west of the Rockies and east of the Cascades," explained George Schaller, a timber sales officer, to those in attendance at one of the Prairie City Ranger District meetings.

"The establishment is a refuge for locals in a slowly withering town," said Schaller. "Seneca suffered a job and population hemorrhage when the sawmill operated by the Hines Lumber Company ceased operations. The logging contracts have become scarce, and fallers must now scrounge for thinning contracts instead of larger timber sales. The entire town is within walking distance of the tavern. Whatever lifeblood is left in Seneca coagulates in that seedy establishment."

The clientele that day featured only locals, except for Leo Anson, the Forest Service timber-marking foreman. Marcia and Joe immediately gravitated to Leo.

Leo greeted them. "Hi, you two. Just back from a wilderness junket?"

"Yep," replied Marcia. "But how can you tell? Must be my perfume," she said with a grin. They all laughed.

"Interesting establishment," commented Joe.

"Yeah, it's a throwback," Leo explained. "They still tell the story about when Bill Winegar, a local cowboy, spread the irate granddaddy of all rattlesnakes on the bar. When the snake recoiled and threatened to strike, all the other cowboys and loggers gathered around, jeering, and spitting toxic bursts of Copenhagen juice at the poor snake's eyes. That's when Bill turned out the lights."

Marcia laughed. "Bet that livened the place up."

"No doubt," responded Leo.

After a couple of beers, Marcia and Joe headed back to Prairie City.

When they weren't roaming the wilderness, Marcia and Joe were inseparable, at least until Marcia would need to return to school shortly after Labor Day. They caught *Blazing Saddles* together at the John Day Drive-In and took trips to Ontario to shop.

But when the time came for Marcia to return to school to study wildlife management at Washington State University in Pullman, Washington, she confessed to Joe that she had a boyfriend back home in Seattle. She explained to Joe that they wouldn't be able to continue their relationship.

Nonetheless, they parted ways amicably and remained friends. Before she left, Marcia invited Joe to visit her in Pullman. "I have a roommate who I would love to introduce you to," she told him. "I think you two would really hit it off."

"I'll be up on the Columbus Day Weekend," promised Joe.

In September 1974, Joe received a letter from Mike Donner, a friend who worked in the Columbia Gorge Ranger District of the Mt. Hood National Forest. Mike invited him on a road trip to Twin Falls, Idaho, to watch notorious daredevil Evel Knievel leap across the Snake River Canyon on a motorcycle. Joe figured he could use a trip, so he agreed.

Evel Knievel was a well-known motorcyclist who staged self-promoted events for a living. He "is probably the only man in history who has become very wealthy by trying to kill himself" by jumping cars, trucks, and other obstacles on his motorcycle, noted *Tonight Show* host Johnny Carson when he interviewed Knievel. He's "a man who has broken more bones than anyone in history."

Even in an era of larger-than-life characters like Muhammad Ali and Elvis Presley, Knievel stood out. After years of jumping cars and busses, he was now planning to jump the Snake River Canyon, so Joe and Mike drove to the Gem State to witness the once-in-a-lifetime event.

Camping overnight at a designated campsite provided by the Sawtooth National Forest, the pair awoke early the next morning and drove to the location of the big event.

Heading north to Twin Falls, Mike and Joe were surprised to encounter a crowd that would rival the Woodstock Music Festival. Apparently, they weren't the only people with the same idea. With the whole world watching on television, Evel Knievel prepared his steam-powered rocket cycle to fly across the canyon in his latest attempt to cheat death.

The first thing that Mike and Joe noticed about the launch site was that the seventy-degree angle of the ramp appeared to be too sharp for Knievel to make it across the formidable canyon. The motorcycle might make it high enough, but it sure didn't seem he could make it far enough to reach the other side. When the cycle ignited, the chute opened immediately, seemingly a miscalculation.

Yet he appeared to make it to the other side until the parachute drifted back into the canyon. Knievel then floated to the bottom of the canyon, landing on the riverbank directly below his launch ramp. He survived the ordeal with only a broken nose.

"I'll bet he had that scam all figured out from the beginning," said Mike, disgusted.

Joe agreed. "A poor showing, indeed. What a total butt job." The pair left immediately to return to Prairie City.

Once the summer had passed, most of the seasonal Forest Service employees returned to school except for Joe. He moved from his summer quarters at the Blue Mountain Work Center in Austin Junction near Dixie Summit to the bunkhouse in Prairie City to work through the fall to the end of his 180-day appointment.

Joe's goal was to save enough money for tuition and rent money to return to school at the University of Oregon during the winter quarter. He was picked up on the timber-marking crew until Christmas when his appointment for the year would expire.

Prairie City Ranger District

In October, Joe received a reminder in a phone call from Marcia. "Joe, you should come up to WSU for the weekend. I'm telling you—you and my roommate, Jan, would be perfect for one another."

"You talked me into it, Marcia," said Joe. "I'll see you this weekend."

Admittedly, the temptation to get the hell out of Prairie City for a few days was enticing. Marcia's friend and roommate, Jan Meyers, also worked for the Forest Service during the summer at the Lake Wenatchee Ranger District, where her family owned a cabin on the south shore of the lake directly across from Dirty Face Peak.

In Pullman, Joe stayed with Marcia and Jan. They toured the campus and then ventured across the Idaho border to Moscow to hit the bars. The drinking age limit was only nineteen, unlike in Washington, where it was twenty-one. So WSU students would flock to Moscow and some of the area's notable bars such as Jekyll and Hyde's.

The trio took flight across the Idaho border for an evening of drinking and dancing. Joe was enamored with Jan and the pair hit it off immediately. As they neared the Idaho border, Marcia cautioned Joe to slow down.

“There’s always a cop on the side of the road ready to gillnet any unsuspecting college students from WSU, so proceed with care, Joe,” said Marcia.

“Will do, Marcia,” he replied. “I don’t need any trouble.”

After a night of fun and frivolity with Marcia and Jan, Joe hit the road back to Prairie City. For the rest of the fall quarter, Joe labored on the timber-marking crew on timber sales in remote parts of the Malheur National Forest.

As the snows flew, the crew was obliged to drive a snowcat to reach some of the assigned timber sales on the books. Right before Christmas, Joe was laid off. He packed his stuff to return to the Willamette Valley, and hit the road for Christmas and New Year’s Day in Portland, and then Eugene for the winter quarter at the University of Oregon School of Journalism.

Flush with cash after six months of working for the Forest Service while living in government housing, he was primed for two quarters of serious schooling. Joe and Jan would continue to keep in touch; a spark had been ignited, and they maintained a regular correspondence during the school year.

CHAPTER THREE

Back to School

Joe's friend Mike Donner, a landscape architecture major at the University of Oregon, had already secured quarters on the corner of 15th and Hilyard Street in Eugene. He invited Joe to join him in renting the basement apartment of a large older home adjacent to campus.

Joe was relieved to have a place to land since he was usually scrambling to find a suitable house or apartment at the beginning of the winter quarter when options were typically limited. He resumed his focus on journalism while continuing his reporting gig covering environmental issues for the *Oregon Daily Emerald*, the campus paper.

At the Hilyard House, the fellows lived in the downstairs apartment. They shared the home with five female students who had their own separate living quarters on the top two stories of the house. Joe and Mike became friends with the young women, who held frequent parties upstairs.

One of the coeds, Nancy Allen, dated Steve Prefontaine, a world-class track star who had already graduated from the University of Oregon but still lived in town. Prefontaine worked as a bartender at a local watering hole known as "The Pad" while training for the Olympics. His competitive nature was legendary. He lived by his mantra: "To give anything less than your best is to sacrifice your gift."

As Joe progressed through his journalism curriculum, he also initiated the process of applying for seasonal Forest Service positions throughout the Pacific Northwest. By April, the offers started pouring in. The first came from the Conconully Ranger District on the Okanagan National Forest—a job on an Inter-Regional (IR) Fire Suppression Crew.

Joe was less than thrilled with the offer because he knew what the job entailed. It wouldn't be pretty, but it could be very profitable. IR crews fight "project" forest fires (large fires requiring an overhead management team) exclusively, and the work is relentless, hazardous, dirty, and exhausting. Not knowing if he would receive any more offers, Joe reluctantly accepted the position.

Soon, Joe started receiving other offers, which kept coming almost daily: positions on the silviculture crew on the Siuslaw, brush disposal crew on the Willamette, IR crew on the Colville, along with more attractive offers as a lifeguard on the Winema and forest fire lookout on the Wallowa-Whitman. With each new position, he would accept the assignment and bail on the previous offer. As the spring quarter ended, Joe was prepared to work as a fire lookout.

Then during the last week of May, tragedy struck in Eugene. Former University of Oregon track star and Olympian Steve Prefontaine died in a car rollover after leaving a post-race party in the early morning hours on May 31, just a few days before Joe and Mike were scheduled to depart for their respective Forest Service seasonal assignments.

"Did you hear that Pre was killed last night in an auto accident?" Mike asked.

"What?' Joe blurted

"It's right here in *The Register-Guard*," Mike noted.

"Holy shit!" said Joe. "This is just awful."

Prefontaine, America's finest distance runner, had just won a five-thousand-meter race the day before at Hayward Field. He then attended a party for six Finnish athletes he had invited to America to compete. After taking Nancy back to the Hilyard House, Pre drove on a residential street near Hendricks Park above the University of Oregon campus at about twelve thirty in the morning.

A police lab analysis indicated that Prefontaine had a blood-alcohol level of 0.16 in his system, higher than what Oregon law allowed. Ironically, Pre may have survived if the car had been lifted off his chest just an inch. The shocking news cast a pall on denizens of the Hilyard House.

The Eugene-Springfield community and the entire state of Oregon reeled in sadness and disbelief. Nancy Allen, Pre's girlfriend, was inconsolable. For Joe and Mike, it was an ignominious ending to an otherwise solid year at the University of Oregon. They adjourned to Taylor's to drown their sorrows over the news of Pre's death.

"Did I tell you that you received another job offer?" Mike asked after drinking a beer.

"No, where from this time?" Joe responded nonchalantly.

"Lake Wenatchee" came the reply.

"You're shitting me, Mike!" Joe exclaimed. "Did you take a message?"

"Well, yeah, it's next to the phone back at the place," he replied. "What's the big deal, anyway? You already have a sweet offer as a fire lookout on the Wallowa-Whitman National Forest."

"Yeah, but this offer involves a girl I met last fall," said Joe. "Hold my beer and save my seat. I'm heading back to Hilyard House. I'll be right back."

Calling the Lake Wenatchee Ranger District, Joe inquired if he had received a call about a job. The receptionist transferred Joe to Faith Hillman, the district's business management assistant.

"Well, yes," replied Hillman. "We have a position offer for you on our trail crew. Are you interested?"

"Yes, absolutely!" confirmed Joe. "Do you happen to have government housing available?"

"Yes," confirmed Hillman, "we'll reserve a spot for you in the bunkhouse. You'll be out on trails most of the time during the season, but you'll have a berth in the bunkhouse when you're not in the backcountry. Very reasonably priced, too."

“That sounds great,” said Joe enthusiastically.

Hillman explained that he would need to report on June 15, two weeks hence. Joe had just enough time to pack his belongings and stop in Portland to see his family before departing for Lake Wenatchee.

As usual, Joe’s car, a 1962 Mercedes Coupe, was unreliable at best.

“It’s cool, though,” he would tell anyone willing to listen. “All-leather upholstery and a four-speed on the column.” True, the inside was nice, but on the outside, it resembled a battle-weary armored vehicle, vintage WWI.

After time with his family, Joe left Portland about midnight heading north on Interstate 5. Stopping briefly at a rest area north of the Kelso-Longview exit, he continued north, turning onto Interstate 405. Suddenly, without warning, one of his tires blew on an offramp. It was two o’clock in the morning, and quite dark. And he was stuck on a narrow flyover connecting two major freeways.

What would he do? What could he do? Pulling his jack and lug wrench out of the trunk, Joe attempted to loosen the lug nuts on the flattened tire. No dice: they were rusted in place.

Suddenly, two Renton police officers pulled up behind his pathetic-looking Mercedes. Joe had never been so happy to see an officer of the law.

“Are you having a problem?” asked one of the cops.

“Yes, I’m in a tough fix,” replied Joe. “I can’t even budge the lug nuts because they’re rusted in place.”

One of the officers retrieved a can of WD-40 from the trunk of the police unit. “Let’s see what we can do here,” he said.

After spraying the lug nuts, the cops tried again and were able to loosen all the nuts. With the tire off, the officers drove Joe to a twenty-four-hour service station, and Joe paid to have the tire repaired while the officers politely waited. The police then drove Joe back to his Mercedes, helping him put the tire back on.

“Thank you so much, officers,” said Joe appreciatively. “You saved my bacon. I must report for work at Lake Wenatchee by morning.”

"You'd best be going then," one officer said.

As he departed the Seattle metropolitan area just before daylight, Joe was dead-tired. He drove to Monroe and made it as far as Baring when the Mercedes inexplicably seized up and ground to a halt. He had the unmistakable sense that his recently acquired vehicle was done for, so he fell asleep in the back until first light.

When the morning sun broke over the ridge, Joe crammed what he could of his belongings into his backpack. Out of curiosity, he peered underneath the frame of the Mercedes to see what he could see. He couldn't believe his eyes. The rear end of the vehicle had been stabilized with two-inch-by-two-inch boards bolted together and lashed with baling wire.

Joe felt a creepy sensation zip down his spine and thought, *that's why the vehicle always felt like it shimmied as I shifted gears! This Mercedes is better off dead.*

By eight in the morning, Joe was on US Highway 2 hitchhiking over Stevens Pass en route to the Lake Wenatchee Ranger Station. When he arrived, he apologized to Faith Hillman for being late, explaining that his vehicle had broken down.

"Will you need any help retrieving your possessions from your car?" asked Hillman.

"Yes, that would be great," replied Joe.

Bob Adamson, a seasonal firefighter on the district, volunteered to drive Joe back to the vehicle to pick up his remaining belongings. When they arrived in Baring, Joe then pulled the plates and abandoned the Mercedes for good.

CHAPTER FOUR

Trail Dog

Now on the trail crew at Lake Wenatchee Ranger District on the Wenatchee National Forest, Joe surprised Jan, who was staffing the reception desk when he walked in the office the next morning.

"What are you doing here, Joe?" she asked.

"I've been hired on the trail crew for the season," Joe announced.

Jan demanded to know, "Why didn't you tell me?"

"I wanted it to be a surprise," Joe said with a wide grin.

"Well, you've certainly succeeded at that," she said, collecting herself. "Let's meet at the Cougar Inn after work for a drink, Joe. We can catch up."

Jan, a fire prevention guard on the district, explained that her friend and colleague, Carol Winters, also managed the bar at the Cougar Inn. Joe nodded enthusiastically. Things were certainly looking up for him after his difficulties on the road.

The Cougar Inn was an old, dilapidated—yet serviceable and picturesque—lodge on the northwest shore of Lake Wenatchee. Oliver and Sally Bates built the two-story structure in the early part of the twentieth century as Lakeview Lodge, hoping to cash in on construction of the Great Northern Railroad through the nearby Chumstick Valley.

Unfortunately, they lost on their gamble when Great Northern chose Stevens Pass and the Nason Creek drainage south of Lake Wenatchee instead. They subsequently sold the hotel to William A. "Cougar Bill" Smith, who renamed it the Cougar Inn in 1922.

The Cougar Inn's grand opening was reportedly attended by the largest gathering ever assembled at Lake Wenatchee, according to the *Leavenworth Echo* archives. Legend has it that Smith walked out the back door of the inn one night and was never seen again. According to the *Echo,* his ghost has allegedly haunted the place ever since.

The Cougar Inn on Lake Wenatchee

After work, Joe and Jan ordered strawberry daiquiris and caught up on their academic endeavors of the past school year. Then Jan, growing quieter, posed the question. "So, Joe, what are you doing here?"

"I applied at several national forests for summer positions," Joe replied. "I had a bunch of offers, but when this position came open, I accepted it because I knew you worked here."

"Uh, Joe," she noted hesitatingly, "I'm sorry to break it to you this way, but I'm in a serious relationship with a guy from Wenatchee. I typically spend my weekends in town with my parents. I hope you're okay with that."

"Yeah, sure, Jan," replied Joe. "No worries. This seems like a beautiful area. I'm looking forward to working as a trail dog."

Joe quickly learned that his "quarters" would be the Forest Service bunkhouse with eleven other seasonal employees, mostly firefighters. He hadn't ever lived with as many people. Joe didn't relish the idea of living in what most on the Lake Wenatchee compound referred to as "the bung-house" because of its generally unkempt nature.

The good news was that Joe would spend very little time in the bunkhouse. He would be out in the backcountry for as many as ten days at a time, so his time spent at the bunkhouse would be brief interludes between trips into the wilderness.

Life on the trail crew would be a rude awakening for Joe. Far removed from his previous gig as a tour guide and boat operator at Crater Lake National Park, this job would be damned hard work.

Here, he would learn the art and science of trail maintenance and construction, while packing horses and mules for "gypsy" crew work on itinerant assignments into the wilderness. He would officially become a "trail dog." Joe worked with Fergus (Fergie) McGregor, the trail crew foreman, and Ike Hobbs, the district packer, shop foreman, and veteran muleskinner.

The first assignments of the season were routine, logging out easy, flat trails close to Lake Wenatchee Ranger Station: South Shore, Hidden Lake, Twin Lakes, and Meadow Creek. Once the snows began to melt in the high country, it was time for overnighters on an extended assignment up the sixteen-mile Rock Creek Trail. A popular drainage for hunters in the fall, Rock Creek would need to be maintained first. On one stretch, a slide had taken out one hundred feet of the trail on a steep hillside and would need to be blasted.

Working around dynamite would be a new experience for Joe. Hobbs was the expert.

Hobbs set the charges and detonated the explosives while Joe and Fergie, stationed as sentries on either end of the blast site, kept their distance and served as spotters. After the section of trail had been blasted, the pair went to work fine-tuning the grade on the trail. Ike mounted his horse and proceeded back down the trail.

"I'll see you two on the other end of the trail at the Carne Mountain Trailhead next week," Hobbs said, without bothering to turn around.

Buck Mountain from Carne Basin

As the crew gradually worked its way up the Rock Creek Trail, Joe learned the hard lesson of what it takes to be a trail dog. The job required skills in maintaining, repairing, building, and rerouting trails—performing every manual task along the way. Most sounded simple, and, in many ways, they were.

They started maintaining the more popular wilderness trails in late spring—logging out fallen trees, clearing rocks from drainage ditches, filling muddy spots, grubbing reroutes around obstacles, and occasionally blasting slides across trails.

Late in the season, the job would shift to larger projects such as building and repairing footbridges over dangerous creek crossings. Most of the work was backbreaking: dig trench, move log, roll rock. Joe would come to learn the tools of the trade: chainsaws, crosscut saws, peavies, axes, rock bars, and shovels.

He would also acquire the requisite skills of a trail dog: sanding a tool handle, sharpening a chainsaw freehand, determining which tree to cut as a bridge stringer. He would learn to pack horses and mules and tie a diamond hitch to secure their loads.

Weather could affect conditions: searing sun and burning heat, pounding cold rain and, at times, light snow—even in the summer in the high country. For Joe, it was quite a shock to his senses.

Then there were the bugs. The trail dogs would need to come to terms with the fact that—in addition to atrocious weather and hard work—they would be dealing with obnoxious bugs virtually all season long.

The first nasty insects of the long bug season are ticks, which tend to follow the snow line in late spring. Ticks are very small, and they will attach themselves to unsuspecting trail dogs, who needed to check themselves thoroughly at the end of the workday.

Mosquitoes are the next variety of flying pests to appear on the scene. Annoyingly ubiquitous, their sheer numbers can be mind-boggling. The good news: mosquitoes avoid trail dogs lathered with "bug dope." Diethylethanolamine (DEET), the active ingredient in bug dope, can deter the thirsty bloodsuckers. The bad news: they are virtually the only bloodsucker among many varieties of wilderness pests that respond to DEET.

The nastiest insects in the backcountry are black flies. A common nuisance in mid-summer, they like to swarm onto unsuspecting trail dogs, looking for any orifice available. Long sleeve shirts and pants offer some respite but not enough. Black flies resemble the common house fly in appearance, but unlike house flies, these bugs bite hard. However, they are slow to establish position, so they're relatively easy to kill. But when they are successful, their bite can hurt for a week.

Deer flies (much like horse flies at lower elevations) are considerably larger than black flies. They appear after the snows melt at elevations of six thousand feet or more in mid-to-late summer. Deer flies have gold or green eyes, giving them an unmistakable "alien" look. Their bite is extremely painful, and can last for weeks.

Last to appear on the backcountry scene in the "dog days" of summer are yellow jackets and bald-faced hornets. Yellow jackets build their nests in the ground, so trail dogs need to be careful where they step. Bald-face hornets nest high in trees. Both varieties are quite nasty, and their stings are extremely painful, lasting for weeks. Yellow jackets and bald-faced hornets are aggressive predators that prey on mammals and even other insects.

All summer long, Joe studied everybody: the lifers, the newbies, and the mule packers. He developed new skills that he would never have anticipated: sharpening chainsaws, peeling logs with a shovel, operating a portable plank sawmill, and dealing with temperamental mules.

His consolation was the beauty of the Glacier Peak Wilderness. Joe would adapt and come to appreciate the life work of a trail dog. His mentors included a unique collection of characters: horse packers and trail dogs from all walks of life.

In the wilderness, Joe and Fergie would occasionally witness the unexpected: topless women hiking along the Pacific Crest Trail and men in camo and grease paint with weapons in their hands and anarchy in their eyes. The trail dogs might stare discreetly while engaging in conversation with the former, but not bother to engage with the latter.

Joe and Fergie enjoyed smoking weed, but marijuana was scarce and hard to find. Yet, there were times when they stumbled on the unexpected. One day, as they approached Grizzly Peak on the Pacific Crest Trail, heading north toward White Pass, Fergie wondered aloud: "Wouldn't it be great if we ran into somebody with some weed who was willing to share?"

"Yeah," sighed Joe. "Now there's a nice daydream."

As Joe responded, he noticed the unmistakable black-and-gray-topped visage of a 35-millimeter film container just off trail.

Thinking that a hiker had lost a roll of film, Joe popped the lid and squealed, "I can't believe it. It's got marijuana in it."

"It does?" responded Fergie with delight.

"Sure does," concluded Joe with a grin.

When they established camp that evening, they fashioned a pipe using a pop can and enjoyed a few hits around the campfire.

In August, Joe and Fergie reverted to bridge building near Lake Julius in the Alpine Lakes Wilderness. Lake Julius would need a new bridge, so they spent two weeks falling trees for sill logs and stringers, cutting the large cedars to size, and then skinning the bark with axes and shovels.

Then, the digging began on either side of the creek exiting the lake. They placed the shorter sill logs on either side of Julius Creek and used a hand winch to move the longer stringers in place. Once the superstructure was complete, they nailed plank boards on top of the stringers. At night, because the weather was cold and miserable, Joe and Fergie huddled in their tent and tried to stay warm. It was much too wet to bother with a campfire.

After they completed that bridge, Hobbs informed Joe and Fergie that another crew member would join them in working on the Estes Butte Trail up the Chiwawa River.

"This job will take three of you," Hobbs explained. "He's a new hire."

"Shit, I wonder if the new guy smokes weed," said Fergie, confiding to Joe that "he may crimp our style."

"We'll just have to wait and see," responded Joe. "It might be okay. Otherwise, we'll just muddle through for another month until our appointments expire."

When he showed up on his first day of work, Paul Kirchmeier seemed like a typical California hippie, laid back about most things but truly enthusiastic working on the trail crew. Loading the mule and the burro into the stock truck, Fergie, Joe, and Paul drove up the Chiwawa River to the Estes Butte Trailhead.

Just before they arrived at their destination, Paul hesitantly inquired, "Do you guys want to smoke a joint?"

Relieved, Joe blurted out, "Hell, yes."

Fergie and Joe had acquired an ideal workmate for the remainder of the season. However, the rest of the day wouldn't be much fun. Their task involved brushing out overgrown ceanothus on a steep hillside in ninety-degree heat. Persevering, they made it to the top to an old lookout site.

After Labor Day, Joe departed Lake Wenatchee to return to Eugene to complete his degree in journalism at the University of Oregon. What he had learned that summer as a trail dog was both unexpected and beneficial. His work ethic improved, and he could see that his efforts as a trail dog had value.

His inner dirtbag also started to emerge. The endurance, strength, and confidence he had developed from long days of work, sometimes in miserable conditions, provided a character-building experience. The skills he learned would serve him well living in any wild place.

Plus, he had dropped thirty pounds from all the hiking and developed muscle throughout his body. Now flush with cash, he could complete his college education with a minimum number of student loans. For Joe, it was a good feeling indeed.

CHAPTER FIVE

Kayaking Pioneer

As Kerry slowly recovered from the loss of his beloved girlfriend Shannon, he delved even further into a new pursuit: kayaking. Living on Puget Sound had its advantages, with easy access to paddling adventures galore.

After buying a kayak from the limited models available, Kerry soon carved out a niche for himself as an outfitter and expedition leader on junkets to the San Juan Islands and Canadian Gulf Islands.

Kayaking the delta wetlands at Lake Wenatchee

Working as a contributing editor for *Kayaking Today Magazine*, Kerry pitched a story to the publication about a trip up the Inside Passage from Bellingham to Southeast Alaska. The editor liked the idea and commissioned Kerry to interview Kelly Tjaden, an educator and outfitter from Anchorage, Alaska, who recently made a solo trip through the passage.

> *Dawn breaks early in the land of the midnight sun. A lone sea kayaker glides quietly across Glacier Bay, a national park known as the undisputed mecca for saltwater paddlers from around the world.*
>
> *Suddenly, a wall of ice dislodges from a nearby glacier, careening and crashing into the bay below. Faced with the dilemma of photographing this natural wonder while preparing for an approaching wave, the solo kayaker accomplishes both tasks. Dodging ice floes to the rhythm of barking seals, Kelly Tjaden is enjoying one of the last great wilderness adventures on earth.*
>
> *Today, sea kayaking has become the fastest growing outdoor pursuit, with an equivalent increase in the popularity of the sport and the number of outfitters offering sea kayaking expeditions. Once the realm of a handful of individuals, sea kayaking is becoming increasingly popular, particularly on the West Coast of North America and Great Britain.*
>
> *Sea kayaking is not, of course, new. For centuries, the sea kayak was an essential vessel for the indigenous inhabitants of the northern latitudes. Modeled after Inuit kayaks used to transport whole families, goods, and sled dogs, the modern sea-touring kayak is designed to carry its passengers safely and silently into the wonder and beauty of the seacoast. Until recently, few had heard of the sport of sea kayaking, let alone experience such an adventure.*
>
> *More recently, however, enthusiasm for the sport has mushroomed, particularly in Seattle and Vancouver, British Columbia—large urban areas near the San Juan and Cana-*

dian Gulf Islands, the Inside Passage, and other protected waterways on the Northwest coast with the potential for exhilarating wilderness experiences.

"Kayak builders in Vancouver and Seattle offer two dozen different variations of this ancient craft," said Tjaden, a Seattle guide for Wilderness Access Outfitters.

"Watching the evolution of the modern sea kayak design over the past five years shows an active process occurring," said Tjaden. "We have rediscovered old knowledge and combined it with new technology to produce an inherently seaworthy boat. Most boat designers now factor ease of tracking, stability, hull efficiency, load carrying capacity, windage profiles, and other considerations into their designs."

Tjaden claims that kayak specialty shops in the Northwest have proliferated in the last few years. Retailers now offer a full line of kayak accessories, classes, seminars, books, and guided excursions from the San Juan Islands and the west coast of Canada to such far-flung destinations as Baja California, Chile, the South Pacific, and Sri Lanka.

Kayak shops stock a wide spectrum of designs including Orca, Heron, Sandpiper, and Eskimo, to name a few. Unique regional trips are offered by licensed outfitters to various locations in the Pacific Northwest, Canada, and Alaska.

"Kayakers use the same waterways as sail boaters," said Tjaden. "For example, the main difference is that kayaks are basically coastal cruisers rather than ocean crossers. But the same skills and rules of seamanship and navigation apply for sea kayakers and sail boaters alike."

However, the sea kayak has several distinct advantages over the sailboat, according to Tjaden. For example, sea kayaking is relatively easy to learn, and the boats have greater accessibility and maneuverability than sailboats.

"You see people paddling all over the San Juan Islands on weekends and along the Seattle waterfront after work," said

> *Tjaden. "The Annual Sea Kayak Regatta in Seattle offers more proof of the sport's growing popularity. This year, the event will be held on August 4. Sea kayaking is basically sailing, canoeing, backpacking, cross-country skiing and bicycling all rolled into one."*

Kerry's editor loved the story. It wasn't long before his articles caught the attention of legendary kayak designer Tom Dern, founder of Eddyline Kayaks, which is based in Seattle. Dern offered Kerry a position as a part-time marketing consultant and kayak designer. This role was an excellent part-time opportunity for Kerry while he attended school.

Eddyline was a leader in the design and manufacturing of sea kayaks, offering the largest variety of boats in the Pacific Northwest and pioneering the vacuum bag and thermoformed kayak technology. In addition, Kerry edited the company newsletter and staffed Eddyline booths at trade shows and outdoor recreation exhibitions throughout the Northwest.

In competitions, Kerry won numerous races in Puget Sound waters, which earned him a reputation as something of an expert in sea kayaking. Despite little formal training, Kerry was inherently talented as a kayak designer and set up his own shop, "Seaworthy Designs," as a side gig.

One day as he marveled at an Eddyline kayak gliding across the surface of the water, he had an idea to create a variation of the craft to enhance its maneuverability. He soon started manufacturing his own sea kayaks that he called Enetai, a Native American term for "where the woods meet the water." His handmade watercraft featured a variety of colors: orange, yellow, bright blue, and British racing green.

Meanwhile, Kerry continued his studies at Huxley on the Western Washington University campus and worked part-time for Skagit County on its comprehensive water management plan.

"Planning is about as political as you can get," Kerry would say, admitting that the conservative politics at the county level irritated him to no end.

Kerry and his mates would fantasize about how to ruin the reputations of certain Skagit County council members by luring them into compromising situations. Soon, however, he would resign from Skagit County for a better opportunity.

Just before Labor Day, Kerry was offered a late-season job on the Lake Wenatchee Ranger District of the Wenatchee National Forest as a water resource technician and part-time backcountry ranger during the high hunt. He would receive school credit for testing and analyzing water sources in the district, thereby contributing to his degree from Western Washington University.

Kerry delved into his new assignment with enthusiasm. He lived in a tent at Dirty Face Campground located behind the ranger station. There, he would hold court with the few seasonal Forest Service employees remaining at summer's end.

He met like-minded crazies both there and in the pubs in Leavenworth, Washington, the closest town to Lake Wenatchee. A tourist mecca with a Bavarian theme, it reminded Kerry of his days in Germany while stationed in the army.

Kerry's time at the Dirty Face Campground didn't last long. He came to spend more of his off-hours in Leavenworth at the bar at the Hotel Tyrol, where he met "Krazy Ken" Navarro. A cook in the hotel restaurant, Ken was a kindred spirit, and he invited Kerry to move into his two-bedroom apartment atop the Tannenbaum Building on Front Street.

"My two-bedroom apartment is too expensive for me on my salary as a cook here at the Hotel Tyrol," offered Ken, "and you need a place to live."

"I'm in," replied Kerry.

Fifteen years before Kerry moved into the Tannenbaum Building, Leavenworth was a remote mountain village ready to wither and die. Mostly a collection of drab, dreary, and dilapidated storefronts, the streets were deserted, and travelers passing through rarely stopped.

But the little town in the virtual center of the state of Washington on the eastern slopes of the Cascade Mountains wasn't always that way.

Leavenworth, initially called Icicle, was a remote log cabin town whose supplies had been ferried over the mountains by wagon and pack animal. In the late nineteenth century, the Great Northern Railway Company, owned by noted "robber baron" James J. Hill, began laying tracks up the Wenatchee River. The railroad soon built a switchyard in Leavenworth, assuring the town's status in the region.

The town of Icicle was platted by the Okanagan Investment Company and renamed for its president, Captain Charles Leavenworth. In 1904, the Lamb-Davis Lumber Company built a large sawmill. Soon after, thousands of apple and pear trees sprang up in nearby orchards, thanks to the construction of irrigation ditches, and a successful fruit industry evolved.

With these developments, Leavenworth became a boomtown overnight and was dubbed by one newspaper as "the wildest town in the West." Drinking and gambling operations thrived, and several brothels opened downtown—one of the largest houses of ill repute in the Tannenbaum Building. With its economic success, the population of Leavenworth soared to nearly six thousand inhabitants, more than nearby Wenatchee, the county seat.

But almost as quickly as it blossomed, the economy of the town tanked after the railroad removed the switchyard and rerouted the tracks through the Chumstick Valley. The stock market crash of 1929, followed by the Great Depression, only made matters worse. Leavenworth sank into ruin. Storefronts were boarded up and the town fell into disarray.

In the early sixties, two enterprising outsiders from Seattle, Ted Price and Bob Rodgers, founded the Squirrel Tree Restaurant about fifteen miles northwest of Leavenworth. The roadside attraction quickly became a popular stop for motorists on Highway 2. The restaurant and resort featured a Bavarian theme based on an idea by Rodgers, who had served with occupation forces after WWII in Munich—the heart of Bavaria.

With their success at the Squirrel Tree, the partners suggested that Leavenworth convert itself into a Bavarian-themed town to turn its fortunes around. In town council meetings, they referenced other struggling communities in the West that had resurrected their economies by converting them into tourist destinations. They pointed to examples like Danish-themed Solvang, California, Dutch-themed Pella, Iowa, and Swiss-themed New Glarus, Wisconsin.

The partners convinced the townspeople of Leavenworth to form the Leavenworth Improvements for Everybody (LIFE) committee and, after a study conducted by the University of Washington Architecture School, the town initiated a plan to "Go Bavarian." They began by converting all the storefronts, and later, virtually all the commercial structures in town into a Bavarian Village.

Fifteen years later, Kerry was living in the former brothel in the Tannenbaum Building with Krazy Ken, both manic characters. The apartment's living room window was adjacent to the town's clock tower, known as a glockenspiel in Bavaria. Kerry and Krazy Ken spent their off-hours at the Hotel Tyrol bar with the Swatsahilee sisters—Tamara and Kamala.

The two Leavenworth residents, well-known nymphomaniacs, would join Kerry and Krazy Ken in their apartment in the Tannenbaum Building for fun and games, consuming mass quantities of cocaine and liquor of all varieties, and fornicating incessantly all night long.

When the snows flew in December, Kerry retreated to Bellingham to complete his studies. Before he left, Kerry invited Paul Kirchmeier, concluding his assignment as a trail dog at Lake Wenatchee, to Bellingham on his return trip to Eureka, California. Paul was also a student, working toward a degree in forestry at Humboldt State. Spending a few days with Kerry, Paul regaled his experiences on the trail crew with Fergie and Joe the previous summer.

"I think I would like those guys," said Kerry. "They sound like my kind of people."

CHAPTER SIX

Crossing the Finish Line

Back in Eugene, Joe was in good spirits. He needed one more quarter at the University of Oregon to complete his bachelor of science degree in journalism. It had been a long road, but the end was in sight. He would graduate just before Christmas. Good thing too because funds were running low. He would soon need to find a real job.

Even though he had a seasonal job waiting on the trail crew at Lake Wenatchee, Joe felt compelled to pursue a career as a newspaper reporter. He applied at several small weeklies and heard back from the *Brookings-Harbor Pilot* on the southern Oregon coast.

Following a phone interview, Joe was hired by the husband-and-wife team of Bob and Dolly Vandehey. Former newspaper journalists from Los Angeles, the couple had purchased the small weekly newspaper in the beautiful beachside community. Joe packed his stuff and drove to Brookings.

Bob and Dolly had converted their garage into an apartment for interns and offered Joe a nice, though rustic, place to live with a kitchen and laundry facilities. He would work as a general assignment reporter and photographer. Bob insisted that he monitor the police and fire radios in his off-hours.

"That's how we find out the hard news," explained Bob. "I want you to keep your ears open when you're off duty."

Joe was amenable at first, but he soon grew weary of the task. Most of the chatter on the police scanner was inconsequential, but

Joe was expected to respond to motor vehicle accidents or fire calls in the interest of finding a story for the next edition.

Joe enjoyed working as a reporter and photographer, but his compensation was meager—only $150 per month—much less than his Forest Service salary. Covering sports and hard news, Joe soon felt like he was spinning his wheels financially. He did enjoy writing features, and every day was different. But some were more challenging than others.

One morning, while typing a routine story, Bob asked Joe to come into his office. "I have a story for you, Joe."

"The police monitor is describing a motor vehicle accident up the Chetco River," Bob explained. "A teenager is trapped in his car in a ditch. The police are planning to extricate him, so take your camera and head to the accident site. You'll see it; a crowd has already gathered around the emergency responders."

"Sounds gruesome," said Joe.

"We've had a real problem with that road ever since it was paved, with teenagers racing the hairpin turns on the fresh asphalt," emphasized Bob. "We need to tell that story."

Armed with directions, Joe drove up the Chetco River and arrived at the scene. As he tried to edge closer to the vehicle with his camera, many in the crowd of onlookers took issue with his presence.

"Who are you?" one asked.

"I'm a reporter for the *Brookings-Harbor Pilot*," Joe replied.

"We don't want you here," came the response.

Joe acknowledged the comment with a nod. Others in the crowd, apparently friends of the victim, voiced their complaints about Joe's presence. He quickly edged closer to the vehicle, snapped several frames using his power winder, and exited the scene to jeers from onlookers.

Man, am I glad to get the hell out of there, he thought. *That was uncomfortable.*

Back at the office, Bob inquired about Joe's experience.

"It was awful," Joe explained. "All the kid's friends and family were there, and they had no qualms articulating their displeasure. A few threatened me if I didn't leave. If cops weren't present, I'm not sure what they would have done to me."

"Good work, Joe," reassured Bob. "Go ahead and write the story. Emphasize the fact that speed limits need to be established and signage installed. I'll develop your film and see what you've got."

The next week, Bob asked, "Joe, have you ever owned a motorcycle?"

"Well, yes, I used to own a Ducati 150, but my mom made me sell it," Joe replied.

"Great!" Bob responded. "I have a story for you."

Bob explained that a group of motorcycle "enthusiasts" had gathered at a Forest Service campground on the Winchuck River. Joe doubted that the idea merited a story in the *Pilot*, but Bob was the boss.

Joe jumped in his truck and drove to the Oregon-California border, turning onto the Winchuck River Road. When he arrived at the campground, Joe discovered that the "motorcycle enthusiasts" were a group of Hell's Angels, the notorious motorcycle club based in Oakland, California. They were holding an initiation rally.

As he approached their camp, red flags went up for some as they noticed Joe, approaching with his camera.

Shit, this could be dangerous, Joe thought, so he proceeded with caution.

"What the hell do you want?" asked one, stopping Joe in his tracks.

"I'm a reporter for the local newspaper," Joe explained. "My boss wanted me to interview some of you for a story in the *Brookings-Harbor Pilot*," Joe explained.

After checking with club leadership, one member told Joe to take a seat next to the campfire ring and wait for the president of the chapter to return from an initiation ritual with new members. Joe sat patiently for the first half-hour Eventually, he grew antsy.

Using his rangefinder to estimate distance with the camera in his lap, Joe snapped a few frames.

Growing suspicious, one member asked, "What are you doing?" It was clear he expected, and would get, an answer.

"Nothing, really, I'm on deadline and need to get back to the office."

Suddenly the leader of the group returned and greeted Joe, who explained his presence at their camp.

"Sure, we'll do a story, but no pictures," insisted the president, who turned out to be quite charming and articulate. He provided Joe with details about their initiation exercise and some general information about their club. Once his interview was complete, Joe expeditiously excused himself and exited their camp.

Mission accomplished, he thought, *and they were none the wiser. Lucky break.*

Developing the film after he returned to the office, Joe was pleased to learn his pictures, despite having to estimate the focus and range, turned out well.

Joe had to hand it to Bob and Dolly. They were not only good editors, but their business acumen was both stellar and ethical, and they certainly got their money's worth out of Joe. On another assignment, Bob had Joe pursue a story on the first girl in Brookings to try out for a Pop Warner football team. To Joe, it seemed like an innocuous assignment. But when Joe contacted the head coach of the team, he responded with vehemence.

"I won't be talking to you about that," said the coach angrily.

When Joe told Bob, the hard-boiled editor and publisher said he really didn't care what the coach said. "Just show up to practice and take your camera."

Joe did what he was told and appeared at Brookings-Harbor High School during tryouts. Fortunately, the coach in question didn't attend the session. When Joe approached the girl's father and asked to take a picture for a story, the pleased parent not only provided a perfect photo opportunity but allowed himself to be interviewed for the story.

Joe ran with the story he had and crafted a piece on the youngster. When the coach learned from some of his assistants what had happened in his absence, he called Joe at the paper.

"If you run that story, I will be pulling all of my advertising from your paper as owner of the town hardware store," he said threateningly.

Alarmed, Joe explained the call to Bob, who looked nonplussed. It was a seminal moment in which Joe learned an important lesson in journalism.

"Joe, this story is news, and we maintain a clear line of demarcation between editorial content and advertising at this paper. If he wants to pull his advertising, so be it. But he won't be doing that. We are the only outlet in Brookings where he can promote his hardware."

Bob called the coach and let him know his position. The story ran as planned in the next edition with no repercussions. The young woman made the team, and the coach never pulled his advertising.

Joe's favorite story was covering three recent University of Oregon graduates—Tim and Kathy Green and Larry Hawkens—who were building a trimaran in the town of Harbor across the Chetco River from Brookings. Their goal, once the giant wooden craft was completed, was to sail around the world. The trio, originally from Paisley, Oregon, had opted for adventure after graduation before they settled down into real jobs. Joe admired their initiative.

"You want to do a story on us?" asked Tim Green.

"Yes, absolutely," responded Joe. "Even my editor agrees this will make a nice feature in the *Pilot*, and I'll include pictures."

"Cool," said Tim. After a lengthy interview with the trio, Tim asked Joe if he wanted to smoke some weed.

"You have weed?' Joe asked, surprised.

"Sure do," replied Tim. In addition to writing what would turn out to be a great feature article, Joe had found a reliable source for marijuana in an otherwise straight town.

Even though he lived rent-free at the Vandeheys, Joe felt like a career working on small weekly newspapers was not the kind of opportunity he needed right now, especially with student loans coming due. The Vandeheys offered Joe a raise, but he had made up his mind. He would return to Lake Wenatchee to pursue a position as a wilderness ranger on the Wenatchee National Forest.

Surely, he reasoned, *he would be welcomed back at Lake Wenatchee.*

Perhaps he could find a new assignment as a lookout or a wilderness ranger, something where he could continue to explore the North Cascades. He called Jan and told her about his plan for the following season now that he had received his degree from the University of Oregon.

"Any chance I can stay at your parents' cabin while I prospect for Forest Service jobs at Lake Wenatchee and in Leavenworth?"

"Of course, Joe," said Jan. "The key to the cabin is on the ledge of the back door." She added, "Just make sure you clean up after yourself before you leave."

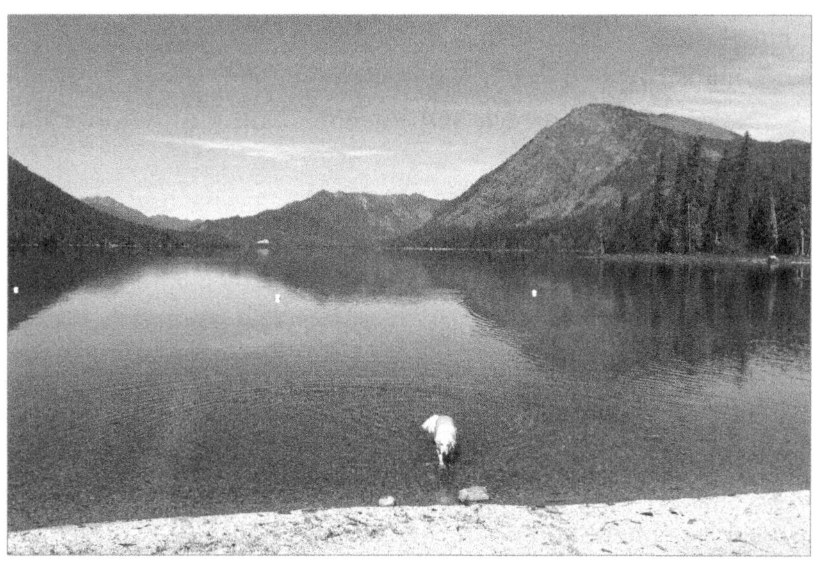

Lake Wenatchee State Park

"Thanks so much, Jan," said Joe appreciatively. "I will definitely clean up the place before I leave."

After a brief stop in Portland, Joe drove eight hours straight through to Lake Wenatchee. Naturally, Seattle traffic added an extra hour to the drive, but he was anxious to arrive before dark, as autumn was quickly descending in the mountains.

Turning onto the south shore drive off Highway 207, Joe arrived at the cabin owned by Jan's family. He located the key and started a fire in the woodstove to heat the place up. He also found a couple of bottles of homemade wine. Jan and her friend, Carol, another fire prevention guard, had bottled the homemade wine during the summer. Pouring a glass, Joe sat on the deck of Jan's lakefront cabin and enjoyed the view.

I could live here year-round, he thought.

The next morning, Joe arrived at the ranger station bright and early and asked to see the Lake Wenatchee Ranger District resource assistant, Dutch Ruitenbeek.

"Dutch just retired," the receptionist replied. "The new resource assistant is Eugene McManus, but he's not in today, although you might be able to catch him at his home on the compound."

"Thanks" replied Joe, "I will do that."

Joe rang the doorbell, and Eugene answered the door. Joe introduced himself.

"My name is Joe Blanco, sir, and I worked on the trail crew here, and I was also a wilderness ranger on the Malheur National Forest the previous summer. I'm just checking to see if you might have any positions in the Recreation Department next season. I've just graduated from college, and I'm looking for a position."

"What did you major in, Joe?"

"Well, journalism," Joe replied somewhat reluctantly.

"Oh, yeah?" he asked. "How would you like a position as lead wilderness ranger? I need someone who can write two management action plans, one for the Glacier Peak Wilderness and one for the Alpine Lakes Wilderness."

"I'd love it," Joe gushed.

"Okay, you're hired," said Eugene. "Fill out the necessary application forms and we'll see you in March."

Spending a couple more days at Jan's cabin, Joe completed the requisite paperwork, then drove back to Portland to collect unemployment for the winter. He was scheduled to report for duty on March 1. Joe was elated. As far as he was concerned, it was a simple matter. The wilderness beckoned.

CHAPTER SEVEN

The Mushroom Haus

In March, Joe returned to Lake Wenatchee, this time as lead wilderness ranger for two of the largest, most remote wilderness areas in the Pacific Northwest. But first things first: he would need a place to live. Joe asked about available housing on the Lake Wenatchee compound, but Carol Winters informed him that all the best rentals were already taken.

"The only housing available is the bunkhouse," she said.

"No way in hell I'm living in the bunkhouse," Joe replied. "I'll set up camp in the Dirty Face Campground before I stay in the bunkhouse."

Carol encouraged Joe to check around the lake and in Plain. "There might be some cabins for rent," she said. "I live in a small cabin myself in Winton."

"Thanks, Carol, I'll do just that," said Joe.

As he scoured the vicinity, Joe stumbled onto a small cabin about a mile west of the ranger station, just across the highway from the Cougar Inn. It was an odd little place with Alice in Wonderland-style mushrooms painted on the side. The front window had a sign: "For Sale. Call Seattle at 732-4197." Joe called the number and inquired about the possibility of renting the cabin.

"Sure," said the owner, "I could use the income. Tell you what, you can rent it until it sells."

"How much will you charge for rent?" Joe asked.

"How about fifty dollars a month?" the owner proposed.

"Sounds good," replied Joe.

He agreed to venture to Seattle to meet the owner, sign a rental agreement, and pick up a couple of keys to the place.

This cabin will be perfect, Joe said to himself.

The Mushroom Haus on Lake Wenatchee

Fergie, the trail crew foreman, volunteered to drive Joe to Seattle to locate the owner, Gene Owens, who lived near the Northgate Shopping Center. Approaching the dilapidated dwelling, Joe began to have second thoughts. But he pressed on because, as he kept telling Fergie, "No way in hell I'm living in the bunkhouse."

Joe knocked on the door. A crusty old guy in a wife-beater T-shirt answered and demanded to know, "What do you two want?"

"Mr. Owens, I'm Joe Blanco, and I called you about renting the cabin."

"Oh, yes, yes, come on in," he said, waving Joe and Fergie inside.

The house was a hoarder's dream. Owens had books and household wares stacked chest high, leaving only pathways through the clutter to a dining room table.

"Here are the keys," Owens offered. "The rent is fifty dollars a month, first and last."

"Here's two hundred dollars for the first four months, Mr. Owens," Joe offered. "I'll continue to send the fifty dollars monthly at your address here in Seattle."

"Fine," Owens said, "and let me know if you want to buy the place. I'm selling it for twenty thousand dollars cash."

"Will do, Mr. Owens," said Joe. "I'll let you know. Thanks so much."

With that, Joe and Fergie retreated back to Lake Wenatchee. As they maneuvered through Stevens Pass, Joe leaned toward Fergie and said, "It's clear this place needs a name. How about the Mushroom Haus?"

"Mushroom Haus it is!" said Fergie with a wry smile.

The cabin had a standard square floor plan, about five hundred square feet on the main floor, with exterior glass on all four sides. The Mushroom Haus featured a wraparound deck with a spectacular view of Lake Wenatchee. The Cougar Inn, located across the highway from Joe's cabin, would prove to be convenient for meals.

The rustic abode had electricity—but no running water—meaning no plumbing nor toilet. An outhouse about one hundred feet up the hill would have to suffice. Heating would be provided by a small wood cookstove, which warmed the cabin adequately but would need constant tending. Joe purchased electric blankets to keep warm after the fire had died down in the evening.

An upstairs loft served as the sleeping area with three beds and modest furnishings. As for water, Joe purchased five-gallon water jugs, which he would fill at the ranger station. He would take showers at the bunkhouse.

Before assuming lead wilderness ranger duties, Joe was to serve as foreman of the tree planting crew in the district during the month of April. Seasonal Forest Service employees were one of two groups that planted saplings in clear-cuts in the district. Independent contractors were the second group. Spring reforestation projects could be brutal, planting Douglas fir and ponderosa pine seedlings on seventy percent slopes in the rain and cold. Sometimes, it would even snow.

Joe's "crew" would include many familiar faces from his previous season on the trail crew, including Jim Perkins, Bonnie Burke, Gottlieb Hille, Dennis Mitchell, Misty Grogan. and Harry Boose. Every morning the crew packed bags of seedlings into the bed of the Forest Service truck and departed for preassigned units near and far—Beaver Creek, Little Wenatchee, Meadow Creek, and other locations.

On the first day of tree planting, Jim Perkins couldn't resist firing up a joint just as soon as the crew had clambered into the cab of the truck.

"Jim," chided Joe, "could you at least wait until we're off the compound to do that? One of the bosses might be watching."

"Yeah, I suppose," came the muted reply.

Tree planting duties typically last four-to-five weeks. Most would agree that tree planting was by far the most difficult Forest Service assignment because of the adverse weather conditions while planting on steep slopes with heavy bags loaded with saplings. Just maintaining footing on some of those slopes can be a challenge. Joe believed that springtime tree planting even exceeded the rigors of fighting forest fires.

Tree planters also must keep a wary eye out for ticks. Springtime in the woods is prime tick season. The parasites belong to the mite family, very small but very nasty. Ticks seek the blood of mammals and can cause Lyme disease among other maladies. Once a tick has found a host, it seeks out any available orifice to drill for blood. As a result, tree planters were instructed to thoroughly examine themselves after a day of planting.

One Friday night after a full day of tree planting, Joe stopped by the Sportsman's Pub for some grub and grog. Coming back to the Mushroom Haus late and tired, Joe plopped into bed without having stopped by the bunkhouse for a shower. Big mistake.

The next morning, wiping his butt after a bowel movement, Joe noticed a squirming tick on the toilet paper struggling to escape. Freaked, he realized the parasite was clearly heading for his anal cavity, which would have been disastrous. He quickly dropped the bloodsucker into the outhouse pit. Feeling lightheaded for a moment, Joe then hastened to the bunkhouse for a belated shower. Afterward, he gathered all his tree planting clothes and washed them thoroughly.

Once the snow receded in the high country, planting season ended, and Joe assumed his duties of working on the management plans for the Glacier Peak and Alpine Lakes Wilderness areas. He had collected examples of plans from other forests as models and spent most of May in the office with his supervisors, Eugene McManus and Raoul Stanford, working on the lengthy documents.

One day Joe received a letter from a friend informing him that one of his climbing mates from the early days had perished on the summit of Mt. Jefferson when he was struck by lightning.

Saddened, Joe thought: *What are the odds? I guess when your number is up, it's up.*

Now working in the office until June, Joe would come to know Jan's friend Carol Winters better. Carol had cofounded a community theater group known as the Plain Players. She asked Joe if he had any interest in joining the group.

"Sure," said Joe. "I was something of a thespian in high school."

"Excellent," replied Carol. "One of our members is having a party soon, and you can audition for the group."

Carol then talked Joe into performing a skit where he would mimic Shirley Temple singing the "Good Ship Lollypop" for his tryout at the upcoming social gathering. The cocktail party would be hosted by Georgia Campbell, a New York socialite and theater aficionado who had relocated to the wilds of the Upper Wenatchee Valley.

Carol gave Joe a cassette recording of the song so he could practice, and she promised to provide the costume, wig, and makeup.

All Joe would need to do is practice lip-syncing the tune. In the evenings after work, he retreated to the Mushroom Haus to practice.

When it was time for the summer season to begin, Carol resumed her position as a fire prevention guard when the district ranger hired a new front office receptionist, Carli Townsend. A music maven, Carli would come to play piano and provide most of the music for the Plain Players.

Meanwhile, Kerry arrived at the Lake Wenatchee Ranger Station for his summer assignment as a wilderness ranger, and his first task was to find a place to live.

By mid-June, most of the better housing options on the compound were already claimed, so he pitched his tent at a campsite in the Dirty Face Campground and reported to the office, where he was greeted by Carli. They hit it off immediately, so Kerry asked Carli if she knew of any rentals available in the area.

"You might check with Joe Blanco," suggested Carli. "He just rented a little cabin down by the Cougar Inn. You can't miss the Mushroom Haus. It has an Alice in Wonderland theme, with mushrooms painted on the sides of the structure."

"Thanks, Carli, I will do just that," replied Kerry.

Dancing around the Mushroom Haus mimicking Shirley Temple to a cassette tape of "The Good Ship Lollypop" in preparation for the tryout, Joe suddenly noticed an odd fellow gawking in one of the many windows lining the deck of the cabin. He looked harmless enough, so Joe waved him to come inside.

"Are you Joe Blanco?" the blond, wiry fellow inquired.

"Yes," replied Joe, "and who might you be?"

"My name is Kerry Weiss," came the response. Kerry and Joe learned they would be working together as wilderness rangers. Though strangers, soon they would become fast friends.

CHAPTER EIGHT

Soul Brothers

What are the chances? Sight unseen, two people eventually connect because another person said, "You've got to meet this guy."

That's the way it happened for Kerry Weiss and Joe Blanco. Call it fate, destiny, kismet. Their meeting was inevitable. Kerry would be one of several wilderness rangers working with Joe patrolling the Glacier Peak and Alpine Lakes portions of the Lake Wenatchee Ranger District that summer. Kerry introduced himself and inquired about housing rentals in the area.

"Right now, I'm living in the Dirty Face Campground above the ranger station," Kerry announced. "But I'm looking for better accommodations than the bunkhouse."

"I don't blame you," Joe replied. "I lived there for one season and it's a trash heap. I found this place, but it's for sale. I haven't seen any other places, though I haven't investigated the area thoroughly. You might check the cabins at Parkside Grocery and the Oxbow."

Kerry and Joe felt an immediate rapport. Kerry was charmed, and he was charming. It simply clicked, and cocktails soon ensued.

Despite their very different backgrounds—Kerry, a ruralist from Dickinson, North Dakota of Scandinavian heritage, with a goal to become an environmental engineer, and Joe, an urbanite of Italian heritage from Portland who planned a career as a journalist—the two had much in common.

Joe and Kerry both enjoyed literature, music, and the arts, and they had similar tastes in food and wine. They both had devoured the works of Jack Kerouac, Ken Kesey, Tom Wolfe, and especially Hunter S. Thompson.

Both men had experimented with psychedelics and marijuana, and they shared a common fondness for Wild Turkey. The two would become fellow wilderness rangers and lifelong friends.

A few days later, after most seasonal employees had arrived for the start of the summer season, management held its first district orientation. All crews were in attendance for the meeting: the trail dogs, brush disposal crew, fire crew, tanker crew, lookouts, prevention guards, and recreation crew.

In the 1970s, these seasonal employees represented a new generation stationed on the front lines. Despite their low rank, they were the heart and soul of the Forest Service, and the public face with users of the national forests. Their challenge was to interface with campers, backpackers, fishermen, horsemen, and climbers who may not always be receptive to the terms and conditions of the federal government.

Subsequent trainings were scheduled and announced. Fire crews would attend "fire school." Wilderness rangers would attend a focused training on backcountry protocols and wilderness ethics. Fire prevention guards, lookouts, and wilderness rangers would complete a course in fire prevention and education.

Before departing for wilderness training, Joe would perform his tryout for the Plain Players. He invited Kerry to join him at an upscale party held at the home of Georgia and Dominic Campbell. Georgia had worked for theater companies on Broadway in New York. Georgia and Dominic, active sponsors of the Plain Players, had retired in Plain.

Entering the Campbell residence on the appointed night, Kerry and Joe were warmly welcomed by the Campbells.

"You must be our entertainment for the evening," Georgia said greeting Joe.

"Yes," replied Joe with a smile. "Carol suggested I audition with a performance of a Shirley Temple tune."

"Yes, thank you for coming, and please help yourself to the bar," said Georgia invitingly, as her husband shook Kerry's hand.

"And what is your name, young man?" Dominic asked Kerry.

"Helmut Vallindaklopf," Kerry replied without hesitation.

"Vallindaklopf?" Dominic asked, surprised. "You must be Finnish! My brother-in-law is a Vallindaklopf. He is a dentist from Tacoma."

Stifling their urge to laugh aloud, Kerr and Joe discreetly bellied up to the bar.

After a couple of drinks and changing into his costume, Joe performed "The Good Ship Lollypop" to an enthusiastic audience. On their way back to Lake Wenatchee, Joe announced, "Kerry, from this day forward, you shall be known as Helmut Vallindaklopf."

"Yes," replied Kerry, "and you shall be known as Doctor Gonzo, a man of letters."

Both Kerry and Joe spoke German, and they soon began to refer to each other as *mein herr* or "sir." That expression eventually morphed into "mein herring."

Back at the Mushroom Haus for a nightcap, Joe and Kerry turned on the television. Much to their delight, *The Eiger Sanction*, with Clint Eastwood, was playing.

"Hey, I love this movie!" announced Kerry. "Let's watch."

"Anything that involves mountains, mein herring," agreed Joe.

Although panned by critics, the movie—Clint Eastwood's first as a director—was destined to be a cult classic. The storyline involves an art professor-cum-hitman, Dr. Jonathan Hemlock (Eastwood), an experienced mountaineer, coerced into taking two last "sanctions" (assassinations) of two vaguely nefarious bad guys.

Set in the Swiss Alps, the plot has Hemlock hired to climb a mountain with an international team to determine which member of the climbing team is the target. When Hemlock asks, "Which mountain?" his contact, a creepy-looking ex-Nazi named "Herr

Dragon," responds, "The Eiger." Joe and Kerry loved the banter between the characters.

"There's our mantra for the season, mein herring," said Kerry.

"Which mountain?" asked Joe.

"Yep," replied Kerry, "as in 'which mountain' will we climb next?"

"I like it," said Joe.

Watching the movie over glasses of Wild Turkey, Joe said, "You never want to find yourself on a climb with someone like Freitag," the greenhorn expedition leader in *The Eiger Sanction*.

"That's for sure," agreed Kerry. "Ego has no place on such excursions. Climbers must choose their partners wisely and avoid those who aren't team players."

Unable to find a rental, Kerry camped at the Dirty Face Campground for the entire season. After work, Kerry and Joe would consort at the Mushroom Haus, engaging in lengthy discussions on art, literature, and especially music. Kerry introduced Joe to a new album by Dan Fogelberg and Tim Weisberg called *Twin Sons of Different Mothers.*

"This shall be our theme for the summer, mein herring," Kerry proclaimed.

CHAPTER NINE

Aldo Leopold Society

With summer underway, Joe believed he had the best job in the world. His weekly "commute" consisted of an eight-mile hike from the old Trinity townsite at the end of the Chiwawa River Road up to Buck Creek Pass, one of the most iconic spots in the entire Glacier Peak Wilderness. His "office" was located at the base of Liberty Cap in a canvas tent near a spring.

His "beat" was the entire upper Chiwawa River and Napeequa River regions. His daily routine required walking the trails, checking for wilderness permits, and warning hikers of hazards. How hard could that be? As a backcountry ranger, Joe met fewer people and responded to fewer calls than the beleaguered fire prevention guards patrolling busy roads and crowded campgrounds.

That summer, Joe and Kerry would come to know the other wilderness rangers: Gottlieb Hille, Ross Roget, and Dylan O. Greisemer, known more commonly as the Dogman. Others joining the confederation at times would include Fergie and his merry band of trail dogs. Collectively, they called themselves the Aldo Leopold Society.

Leopold was an American forester, naturalist, ecologist, and environmentalist who was influential in the movement for wilderness. A professor at the University of Wisconsin, Leopold is best known for his book, *A Sand County Almanac.*

"I like it," pronounced Gottlieb. "Very fitting title for this group."

At the beginning of every season, the Mt. Baker-Snoqualmie and the Wenatchee National Forests conducted a three-day wilderness training session for seasonal wilderness rangers assigned to patrol the Alpine Lakes and Glacier Peak Wilderness Areas. Attending the session were seasonal rangers from the Naches, Tieton, Ellensburg, Cle Elum, Leavenworth, Lake Wenatchee, Entiat, and Chelan Districts.

Buck Mountain, Mt Berge, and Mt. Cleator

This year's session would be held at Ingalls Lake in the Alpine Lakes Wilderness, so Joe and Kerry began coordinating the trip south to the Teanaway River Valley. In preparation, they huddled at the Mushroom Haus to plan for the training.

"Shall we bring some hootch?" Joe proposed.

"Of course, mein herring," said Kerry. "I'll bring the rum and you bring the strawberries. With a little snow, we'll make strawberry daiquiris. We'll just mash the strawberries in the snow."

"And some weed?" Joe continued.

"Goes without saying," came Kerry's reply.

In addition to wilderness rangers, Carli Townsend would tag along on the training. She was interested in understanding what the rangers would learn to become more educated in providing guidance and directions to the public. A fortyish blonde with no backpacking experience, she was nonetheless in good physical shape. Kerry and Joe were fond of Carli because she was good-natured and "fun to be around." How she would do on the excursion was anybody's guess.

On the first day of the training, Joe prepared the Forest Service truck and the crew departed for the Ingalls Lake Trailhead. They drove down the Tumwater Canyon to Leavenworth, then over Blewett Pass to the end of the Teanaway River. Carli drove her own vehicle and met the crew at the trailhead.

"How far of a hike are we looking at?" she asked Kerry.

"Only about three miles, but it's a steady uphill climb to Ingalls Pass," replied Kerry. "Are you up for this?"

"Absolutely!" Carli replied without hesitating, upbeat as ever.

Hikers trekking down the Ingalls Lake Trail might have mistaken the group as a mishmash of Mt. Stuart-bound mountaineers and twenty-something hippies. But make no mistake: this group was a cadre of elite backcountry rangers disguised as dirtbag climbers—an apt description that most would admit to readily.

Most seasonal rangers were college students. After working in the woods for a few years, they would then move on to other careers or apply for permanent positions in the US Forest Service or National Park Service. In some cases, these seasonal "temps" actually became more permanent than the "permanent" employees, who were frequently transferred to other forests or parks.

Some rangers already held degrees in forestry, geology, philosophy, art history, or like Kerry and Joe, environmental science, and journalism, respectively. Some were teachers, writers, photographers, ski instructors, winter guides, and documentary filmmakers. They were all adventure seekers who, for whatever reason, were working as seasonal wilderness rangers. They wore many hats as geologists, naturalists, botanists, wildlife observers, and local historians.

Wilderness rangers were also required to fill out reports, such as trail logs and monthly dispatches, summarizing activities and observations in the backcountry. At the end of the summer, they would compile their findings in a year-end report.

The most ridiculous form a wilderness ranger might be asked to complete was the "negative report." The form, documented as FS 1300-22, was often required to assure the receiving office that the reporting requirement had not been overlooked. Unless reporting instructions specifically stated that a negative report is not required, "this form should be submitted when there is nothing to report."

"We could have some fun with this one, herring," Joe mentioned to Kerry.

"Yeah," replied Kerry. "We'll have to come with something original, something creative, something gonzo."

"You mean like 'Tales of Tater Boy,' perhaps?" Joe proposed, recalling their parody of life in the Tri-Cities.

"Precisely," said Kerry.

Rangers from the various districts arrived at the trailhead at different times on the appointed morning and hiked to the rendezvous point at Ingalls Lake. Halfway up the trail, Kerry sensed that Carli was struggling, mostly due to new boots that chafed at the back of her heels. Kerry quickly jogged to the pass, dropped his pack, and walked back down the trail to help Carli. He hoisted her backpack and carried it to Ingalls Pass.

"Thanks, Kerry," Carli said appreciatively.

Ingalls Pass revealed a stunning view of Mt. Stuart and the Stuart Range, which are part of the Wenatchee Mountains. Below the pass was Ingalls Lake, a small mountain tarn reflecting the image of Mt. Stuart.

After introductions that evening, wilderness rangers had free time to prepare a meal or explore the area. With plenty of daylight left, Kerry, Joe, Gottlieb, Ross, and the Dogman summited Ingalls Peak, a relatively small knob west of the Ingalls Pass. From the top, they marveled at the sun setting on the western horizon.

Afterward, it was time to eat and break out the daiquiris.

"Do you have the rum, mein herring?" asked Kerry.

"But, of course," Joe replied. He packed the strawberries into the pot from his mess kit, but the mashing process was difficult because of the cold. He added the rum anyway.

"Daiquiri?" Joe offered with a laugh. "It's my favorite. Chunky style." When offered a drink, Carli was polite but took just enough to taste. Although she was known to enjoy an occasional glass of wine, Carli wasn't much of a drinker.

The next morning, the training began in earnest. Participants learned that wilderness rangers would perform the usual tasks—checking for wilderness permits, posting new signage, and, in an emergency, tending to situations as best they could and radio for assistance, if necessary.

Of course, wilderness rangers would also preach the gospel of low-impact camping and treading lightly on the environment, particularly in meadows and near mountain lakes. A common refrain among wilderness rangers was "take nothing but photographs, leave nothing but footprints."

Another frequent chore was to dismantle fire pits, some that resembled "fire castles." Some fire pits even had iron grates that campers had previously stashed for future use. Generations of hunters had been coming to these popular spots for decades.

Yet wilderness rangers would learn that their primary duty was to collect garbage—lots of garbage. Particularly during "high hunt," the early season hunt that is open only in wilderness areas, hunters would pack supplies in with horses and mules, leaving much more behind than any backpacker could carry—large rolls of visqueen (black plastic), frying pans, and more.

Another task was cleaning up "improved" campsites, which meant tearing down log-and-rock dining tables and kitchen areas. Rangers also learned how to protect their supplies from critters in the backcountry.

"All food should be stored away from your campsite and tied to a rope slung over a branch," noted Carl Dorell, the recreation staff officer at the Wenatchee National Forest Supervisor's Office, in a serious voice. "A metal food storage container is even better. This includes food and everything that smells like food, such as chewing gum, breath mints, toothpaste, sunblock, and shampoo."

The training concluded with a four-hour session on cardiopulmonary resuscitation (CPR) and an overview of the incident command system for search-and-rescue operations (SARs). These emergency exercises might involve locating lost persons and rescuing individuals in a medical emergency.

The next morning the band of wilderness rangers packed up and headed back down the trail to return home to begin their season in the wild. However, for the Aldo Leopold Society, one more training awaited—a week-long session on fire prevention in Ellensburg held at Central Washington University.

Wilderness rangers, fire prevention guards, and lookouts—the job classifications that had the most interaction with the public—would attend the session. The training had an intensive customer relations focus, in addition to an overview of law enforcement. Kerry was particularly excited about the week in Ellensburg.

"I attended Central Washington University for a year, mein herring," he informed Joe. "I know that town like the back of my hand."

Once again, the crew of Kerry, Joe, Gottlieb, Ross, and the Dogman piled into the "six-pack" Forest Service truck for another training junket. Upon arrival, they were each assigned a dormitory room on campus. Central Washington University is a mid-sized four-year educational institution that opened in 1891 with a focus on educating future elementary and high school teachers.

En route to Ellensburg, Kerry told the group: "This school is definitely in the party mode. We should have a lot of fun on this gig."

The five-day training emphasized fire suppression and prevention, as well as customer and public relations. The training reinforced what they had learned about law enforcement, the incident command system, and search-and-rescue operations.

At the end of the first day, a group of like-minded individuals hatched a plan to paint the little college town red. Guys and gals from Chelan on the north to Tieton on the south met at The Cornerstone, a popular college bar in Ellensburg. The beer flowed as the jukebox wailed to the strains of Tom Petty and the Heartbreakers singing "Breakdown."

Joe struck up a conversation with a lookout from the Naches Ranger District named Rachael White, and the two played pool while the party continued. Eventually, the entire group relocated to the Ranch, a dance bar on the edge of town.

On a particularly warm day near the end of the training, a collection of Forest Service seasonals retreated to a park on the Yakima River to cool down with a swim, followed by more bar-hopping that night.

"Joe, you should come see me up on my lookout," suggested Rachael. "It's on Little Bald Mountain up the Naches River. It has a spectacular view of Mt. Rainier from the east."

"I'd like that," replied Joe.

Their training regimen complete, the Aldo Leopold Society drove back to Lake Wenatchee.

CHAPTER TEN

Napeequa Crossing

On the following Thursday morning, Lake Wenatchee Resource Assistant Eugene McManus popped downstairs from his second-floor office—in his stocking feet as usual—to ask Carli who would be where in the backcountry. Thursdays are the first day of the work week for wilderness rangers in high season.

"Carli, do you know where Weiss and Blanco will be this weekend?" inquired Eugene.

"Do we ever really know where those two will be?" Carli asked with a laugh.

"True," Eugene said with a sigh. "I think they said something about the Napeequa River area."

"Joe left me a note saying he would be hiking to Little Giant Pass," stated Carli, "and Kerry told me on his way out he would camp in Boulder Basin before dropping into the Napeequa."

"Well, at least they check in with you, Carli," said Eugene, with a smile. "I'm merely their boss. But I'm glad they'll be in the Napeequa. We haven't had a ranger patrol that far corner for years."

The Napeequa River Valley, called the "Shangri-La of the Cascades," is one of the most remote and inaccessible areas of the Glacier Peak Wilderness. The valley features steep canyon walls and glaciated peaks requiring a climb of over four thousand feet of elevation gain just to have a peek.

Napeequa River Valley: The Shangri-La of the Cascades

From both Boulder Pass and Little Giant Pass, the views of the Napeequa River are breathtaking. But access to these passes presents its own set of challenges. Protected by deep snowpack for most of the year, the bridgeless river can be treacherous to cross when the current is raging in early summer.

Later, swarms of ravenous black flies can overwhelm unsuspecting backcountry travelers. Consequently, the Napeequa River remains an obscure, quiet place with few visitors. Kerry and Joe planned to meet at the junction where the Boulder Pass and Little Giant Pass trails intersect at the Napeequa River.

On Thursday, Joe forded the Chiwawa River over a logjam to the abandoned Maple Creek Campground and hiked up the Little Giant Trail to the pass, where he camped the first night. Meanwhile, Kerry hiked into Boulder Basin. On Friday morning, Kerry and Joe rendezvoused before noon at the Napeequa Ford junction and continued hiking upriver to a well-established campsite at the junction of the Napeequa River and Louis Creek.

Setting up camp, Joe asked Kerry, "Which mountain, mein herring? You up for climbing Buck Mountain?"

"Hell, yes," replied Kerry. "That's why we signed up for this hootenanny. We're out here to patrol the area and climb mountains."

The camp at Louis Creek was well established, so they completed a code-a-site form on the location as instructed. The next morning, they left camp early to climb Buck Mountain. Scaling the tangled slide alder along Louis Creek, they found the going challenging, with steep brush and waterfall after waterfall. Once past the brush, the route leveled out on the low-gradient southwest flank to the summit.

Buck Mountain, one of the two highest peaks in the Chiwawa Mountains, features spectacularly magnificent quaquaversal views. Gazing down the precipitous north face of the mountain took their breath away.

"That would be a long fall," Kerry said.

"Yeah," said Joe. "Freaks me out just being close to the edge."

Directly below the summit on the north side sat King Lake. Since they were at a high altitude, Joe checked in with the ranger station by radio. After an hour on the summit, they descended to their camp at Louis Creek.

"What a trip," reflected Kerry. So far, the rangers had yet to see another living soul.

The next morning, they broke camp and followed the trail upriver and reached the north fork of the Napeequa, which drains the large hanging valley below High Pass. Ascending uphill through slide alder, they reached the narrowing basin leading to the 7,100-foot High Pass.

As the day wore on, the heat became unbearable, with temperatures reaching 102 degrees Fahrenheit. As they approached the upper basin, a thunderstorm surprisingly blew in from the west. Suddenly, the temperature plummeted to 51 degrees Fahrenheit. Lightning strikes and hail peppered the basin indiscriminately.

Clark Mountain from North Fork Napeequa

Becoming increasingly confused and disoriented, Joe started shivering incessantly. "I don't feel so good," he muttered to Kerry.

"Let's just get to the pass," encouraged Kerry, alarm bells ringing in his head. Kerry could see the telltale signs of hypothermia settling in with Joe, who hadn't been consuming enough water.

When they reached High Pass, Kerry immediately went to work setting up their tent and laying out their sleeping bags. He then fired up the cookstove to make tea and told Joe to crawl inside the bag and keep his down coat on. The tea helped, but when he continued to shake, Joe rolled a joint and fired it up. The shivering stopped immediately.

Just then, the storm passed, and the sun peeked out from the west over Glacier Peak like a vision from the end of times.

Joe and Kerry then prepared dinner while appreciating the views of Glacier Peak and of Triad Lake below High Pass. Rising early the next morning to sunny skies and warm temperatures, they packed their camp and hiked to Buck Creek Pass, where they finally encountered the first signs of other trekkers since they left on their excursion to the obscure corners of the Glacier Peak Wilderness.

After a night at Buck Creek Pass, they hiked the busy route to the trailhead at Trinity and started looking for a ride. A couple of dirtbag climbers gave them a lift in the back of their pickup to the Maple Creek Campground, where they jumped in Joe's Forest Service rig and headed back to Lake Wenatchee.

"Let's hit the bunkhouse for a shower and a shave before we head to the Mushroom Haus," suggested Joe. "We'll have to report in at the ranger station anyway."

"Capital idea, mein herring." responded Kerry. "And after, we should take a trip to the Bavarian Village to hit the liquor store. We must toast our conquest of Buck Mountain when we return to the Mushroom Haus."

CHAPTER ELEVEN

Peak Performance

Mid-summer is peak season for wilderness rangers. The backcountry has finally lost most of its snowpack and the mountains are accessible to backcountry hikers, campers, and climbers alike.

For the Aldo Leopold Society, it was prime time and there was plenty of work to do installing Wallowa toilets (wooden boxes on a small platform positioned over a deep pit), hanging new signage where necessary, and digging out water bars on high routes. Rangers also conduct other minor trail maintenance tasks, check hikers for wilderness permits, and generally provide a Forest Service presence in the backcountry.

For their first task that summer, the Aldo Leopold Society worked as a team, building and installing new Wallowa toilets in Spider Meadows in upper Phelps Creek, a popular spot for wilderness users in the upper Chiwawa River area.

Packing the wooden components and tools necessary to build the rustic privy, the group established their campsite before proceeding to the locations designated for new pit toilets. With enough manpower, the group completed the assignment expeditiously, with plenty of time remaining for other activities.

Around the campfire that night, Kerry looked at Joe, and then the others and announced: "Gentlemen, we have a decision to make: Which mountain?"

With dozens of tall peaks on the Lake Wenatchee Ranger District, backcountry guards qualified as climbing rangers. They all had received training in crevasse rescue techniques, equipment usage, and review of new techniques and devices. They also learned skills in implementing load-releasing hitches, single and multiple anchors, and patient transport via sled or helicopter.

Increasingly, backcountry travelers with little-to-no mountain experience would attempt to climb peaks in the wilderness, and the Aldo Leopold Society had been charged with patrolling climbing routes in the district.

With mountain options galore adjacent to Spider Meadows, the group, which included Kerry, Joe, Gottlieb, and the Dogman, chose Mt. Maude, a nine-thousand-foot peak in the Entiat Range. Setting up camp in Leroy Creek basin, the climb required an early start before the sun could melt the hardened snowpack that makes the route easier to negotiate.

After a few hours, the group reached the summit, consisting of mostly talus with small rocky outcroppings. The south face features a relatively mild slope compared to the north face, a Class Four climb with exposure and steep inclines requiring ropes.

Mt. Maude and Seven-Fingered Jack from Carne Mountain

For the uninitiated, it may sound simple: climbing a peak to its summit. Every mountain has one. But for Joe, the point of a climb is the process and the experience of venturing to remote places that few people get to experience for themselves.

"The adventure is about climbing, not just summiting," Joe would remind anybody willing to listen. "It's the journey, not the destination."

Like many of his role models such as Reinhold Messner, Joe believed in the concept of a measured approach to climbing. Although he enjoyed reaching the summit of a mountain, Joe wasn't merely interested in the "conquest" aspect.

"It's easy to forget that climbing is trial and error," Joe said. "Sometimes, we summit. On other days, we manage to make it part way but retreat due to a lack of time or bad weather. Personally, I'm not interested in climbing in a whiteout. Sometimes, a good reason to turn back is altitude sickness or injury."

That summer, Kerry and Joe would make two attempts on Glacier Peak, the largest mountain in the vicinity. Their first attempt from the east seemed straightforward enough in the *Cascade Alpine Climbing Guide* by Fred Beckey.

But with only four days to climb, they seriously underestimated the time needed to complete the task. They took two days just to reach the remote base of the mountain in the upper Suiattle River Valley. Nonetheless, Kerry wanted to push on to attempt to summit despite a lack of time.

"No dice," Joe said firmly when Kerry suggested they continue. "We'll never make it."

On their next attempt, Joe and Kerry would have considerably more time to summit Glacier Peak. Working on installing puncheon—or wooden planks—over bogs and conducting drainage work in Meander Meadow at the headwaters of the Little Wenatchee River, they completed their mission ahead of schedule. Already close to the south shoulder of Glacier Peak, they scaled the easiest summit route up Sitkum Glacier.

On the summit, Joe marveled at the view. “We can damn near see the whole state of Washington from here.”

“We’re lucky we climbed today,” said Kerry. “Fred Beckey wrote that Glacier Peak has only thirty clear days on the summit a year.”

“Out timing was perfect,” Joe concluded.

On the way down the mountain, Joe and Kerry encountered a confused and disoriented climber at the base of a boulder field.

“Are you okay?” Kerry inquired.

“No,” said the climber. “My partner and I were negotiating this boulder field when all hell broke loose in a rockslide. I’ve been trying to locate him, but my friend is buried underneath these boulders.”

Joe quickly radioed the Lake Wenatchee Ranger Station to initiate a search-and-rescue operation. Then the two rangers waited with the climber on a flat spot below the boulder field for the rescue team to arrive by helicopter. Sadly, the missing climber was eventually located but he had been crushed between the massive boulders. Still alive when evacuated by the helicopter, the climber later died at Central Washington Hospital in Wenatchee.

On their way back to Meander Meadows, Joe and Kerry discussed the concept of climbing as a competition.

“As you know, herring, I like adventure,” said Joe. “I’ve always wanted to visit the last great wilderness environments and explore mountains where others can’t get to easily. But for me, I don’t consider climbing as a sport. I want to test my limits, but it’s not a competition. I’m not interested in killing myself.”

“I don’t know, mein herring,” replied Kerry. “We must recognize that death is always a possibility when we climb. If it’s not a possibility, it’s not mountaineering. The art of mountaineering is risk-taking. I realize my views on this subject may be demented to many, but my lust for life comes from putting my life in danger. Some see that as a problem.”

Joe knew that Kerry was manic from the moment he met him. But now he was coming to learn that Kerry was fearless to the point of recklessness, and he often wondered why. Joe had a few clues to the inner workings of Kerry's psyche, but the puzzle was far from solved.

"Sorry, herring, but we must agree to disagree," countered Joe. "To me, mountaineering is the art and science of not dying."

At the end of the summer, Joe—as lead wilderness ranger—filed his "season report," covering topics such as wilderness administration, user relations, and environmental elements, while providing recommendations for improvements. In addition to patrolling the wilderness, ranger duties also included coordinating volunteer projects with Outward Bound and Northwest Outdoor Leadership School, summer wilderness programs for youth.

That season, Outward Bound had volunteered to provide much-needed trail maintenance on the Little Giant Trail into the Napeequa River drainage, a narrow, unmaintained trail that had proved troublesome for horses during "high hunt." Joe and Kerry had met early in the season with Jim Miller, director of Outward Bound, and his teenage protégées to provide training on how to conduct trail maintenance.

After a daylong training with Outward Bound at the Maple Creek Campground, Joe and Kerry stashed a cache of tools at the Maple Creek Cabin for the volunteers to use. However, by the end of the season, nothing had been accomplished on the Little Giant Trail.

In his end-of-the-season report, Joe noted that "even though we spent a considerable amount of time prepping and training the volunteers, absolutely nothing was accomplished on the trail. Jim Miller, the Outward Bound director, reported back that 'due to injuries and bad weather,' the Little Giant project was never attempted."

"This makes the second summer in a row that Outward Bound failed to perform maintenance on the Napeequa River side of the Little Giant Trail," Joe wrote. "Admittedly, the care and maintenance of volunteers is tricky business. Moving forward, Outward Bound service projects should be monitored closely to assure completion."

Individually, the Aldo Leopold Society also worked with private outfitters who utilize horses and pack strings to provide wilderness access for clients. The outfitters, all experienced trail hands, file permits with the Forest Service to accompany groups into the wilderness. Outfitters make a decent living during the summers and are often quite busy. On the Lake Wenatchee District, the two primary packers were Vince Schapp and Roy Gwartney.

Schapp lived with his wife and daughter in an old school bus parked on a Chelan Public Utility District right of way by permit. You wouldn't know it by his scruffy appearance, but Schapp was a hard-working outfitter who secured large contracts with various and sundry well-heeled clients.

Roy Gwartney, based in Stehekin, Washington, on Lake Chelan, was another popular outfitter. A consummate professional, Gwartney visited the Buck Creek Pass area often, so Joe would engage him frequently. Gwartney was well versed in Forest Service rules, regulations, and protocols.

Joe's report also covered an overview of range management issues. Every summer, Basque sheepherders would drive bands of sheep from the Yakima Valley to graze in the high mountain meadows of the Lake Wenatchee District, as part of the Forest Service philosophy of multiple use of national resources.

"I walked most of the sheep driveways in the upper Chiwawa drainage this summer," Joe continued in his report. "As in the past, the Martinez band utilized the Rock Creek drainage, which benefited hikers by clearing brush along the trail."

"Ironically, most backpacker feedback concerning the presence of sheep was negative," he wrote. "Hunters, on the other hand, were indifferent or felt the presence of sheep had little effect on their wilderness experience. The Martinez sheepherders were an enthusiastic and hard-working group of individuals."

CHAPTER TWELVE

Port Season

Wilderness rangers would come to recognize the approaching autumnal equinox as a vaguely uncomfortable and oddly awkward cusp between summer and fall. Sadly, summer was on the wane, and there was an unmistakable sense the door was closing on adventures in the high country for the season.

To deal with the approaching sense of loss, Joe and Kerry introduced a new ritual to cope with the weirdness: drinking cheap, disgusting port wine from the local market during this curiously tentative time of the year. The Aldo Leopold Society came to refer to this period—when most seasonal employees return to college—as port season.

Not quite summer and not quite fall, this transition can translate into bizarre endings and beginnings, unsettling events in the form of sudden changes, disappointments, and revelations.

"Even if you can't see it," Joe would say, "you can feel its effects."

It's mostly a period of strange, kooky, and rather bizarre anomalies on several fronts. Some incidents are earth-shattering, some are simply vague and uncomfortable, but all are peculiar.

That September, Keith Moon, the drummer for The Who, succumbed to an overdose of drugs and alcohol. It would be the first omen of the onset of bad juju to come. The Who was Joe's favorite rock band.

"Do you remember the album cover from *Who Are You?* mein herring?" asked Joe.

"Not exactly, why?" replied Kerry.

"Three members of the band are standing," explained Joe, "but Keith Moon is sitting down backward with the words 'Not to be taken away' stenciled on the back of his chair."

"A bad omen, mein herr," observed Kerry.

That night, during a pounding wind and rainstorm, district personnel received a radio call: the dreaded 10-0, meaning a fatality. All available personnel were summoned immediately to the Lake Wenatchee Ranger Station. Gathered around in the Fire Warehouse, crews learned that four massive trees had fallen on a small travel trailer at Riverside Campground, trapping four hunters.

With personnel packed into every available vehicle, they drove up the Little Wenatchee River to the site of the tragedy. Floodlights powered by generators ringed the campground as crews used chainsaws and winches to breach the logjam of timber blocking access to the small travel trailer.

"Jesus," cried Kerry. "This looks like a set of jumbo pickup sticks."

"What a disaster!" replied Joe, as they cut and stacked the live green branches from the twisted mass of uprooted Douglas firs burying the flattened metal.

More than thirty Forest Service staffers worked until dawn to gain access to the crumpled travel trailer. Afterward, all who remained were Washington State police officers and Chelan County sheriff deputies to survey what was left. Sadly, all four hunters had perished.

The on-scene investigation was routine. Take photos. Make a few measurements. Scribble notes onto yellow notepads. Put the bodies in bags. Put the bags on "stokes litters," also known as basket stretchers. Hook them to lines on the helicopter. Give the helicopter pilot a thumbs-up for clear takeoff and cordon off the area with yellow caution tape. Conversations were muted among responders.

As they headed back to the ranger station in their vehicle, Kerry asked Joe, "Do these situations ever bother you?"

"Of course," Joe replied. "Death is never painless."

A week later, as Joe helped Kerry pack in preparation to return to school in Bellingham, Lake Wenatchee District Ranger William Bertleson ordered a search-and-rescue (SAR) operation to find Scott Foresman, a seasonal employee reported missing after failing to show up at work for four days. Foresman had been living at one of the small trailers on the compound; he had lately been working in the office on light duty. All available personnel were activated to comb the entire Lake Wenatchee District.

Eventually, his car was found at the end of an obscure road up the Little Wenatchee River that ended in a clear-cut. Inside his car, searchers discovered a copy of Fred Beckey's *Cascade Alpine Guide,* with the page open to the climbing route to Mt. Massif; the route had been circled. Once the car was located, district staff combed a wide swath of terrain on each side of the vehicle above and below.

Taking a break from beating through the brush, Kerry asked Joe, "Did you know this guy?"

"Yes," Joe responded, solemnly. "It's a sad tale indeed."

"He was a forestry technician like the rest of us, but he worked in timber, setting up sales," Joe continued. "Smart guy. Scott graduated from Cornell University with a degree in statistics. He was a skilled rock climber and had been selected for an elite team of cone pickers who climb trees using spikes and harnesses to harvest high-quality cones to produce seedlings."

"One day after work, he was practicing his climbing techniques on the compound," Joe added. "He was about ninety feet up a Douglas fir when he inadvertently bumped a nest of bald-faced hornets. They attacked him relentlessly, and he had to release his harness to escape, falling to the ground and breaking practically every bone in his body," Joe said, shaking his head.

"That's bloody awful!" gasped Kerry.

"Yeah, but the worst part was he had no medical insurance and had to rely on worker's compensation," said Joe. "He was never the same after his fall. He was in constant pain. My hunch is that he took his own life."

"I could see pulling the plug in that situation," said Kerry. "I'd do the same. I've fantasized about the prospect of taking myself out, if and when it's necessary."

"Really?" replied Joe, shocked at Kerry's comment. "I can't imagine. I grew up Roman Catholic. I will suffer until the end rather than take myself out. The nuns drilled it into our heads; suicide was the worst possible sin of all. Do not pass go, do not achieve life everlasting."

"I don't believe in such nonsense," replied Kerry.

That abruptly ended the conversation, and they resumed their search. Subsequent searches that season failed to turn up any sign of Scott Foresman.

For the remainder of the fall season, Joe was reassigned to the recreation crew with Flynn Stein, the foreman. As the result of the tragedy at Riverside Campground, the forest supervisor ordered ranger districts to remove all dead tree snags within one hundred feet of every campground. Together, Flynn and Joe would spend the next two months cutting down every dead tree at every campground in the district.

On their first day, Raoul Stanford, the recreation supervisor in the district, instructed Joe and Flynn to meet him at the Grouse Creek Campground to demonstrate how to cut down large snags. Scouting the campground, Raoul immediately spotted a Douglas fir with a dead top within the prescribed radius.

"Here's a great example of a fir that's not completely dead but is mostly gone," said Raoul. "We would consider this tree a hazard for removal."

The thirty-six-inch diameter Douglas fir was well over one hundred feet tall. A skilled faller, Raoul initiated his undercut while Flynn and Joe worked as spotters, keeping the public from harm's way, and driving wedges as needed to facilitate the cut. As Raoul began his back cut, the large fir teetered, then swung sideways.

Just then, Flynn yelled out, "It's starting to go!"

Unfortunately, the snag started to "barber chair" sideways, in logger parlance, due to its rotten core. In such cases, trees violently split and teeter overhead, then fall in the opposite direction than what was intended. The large fir squarely hit the Grouse Creek Campground outhouse, splintering the structure into smithereens, and sparing only the toilet.

"The core was rotten," announced Raoul with a sheepish grin.

CHAPTER THIRTEEN

Winter Solitude

Working together through the autumn months, Joe and Flynn continued cutting and splitting firewood, mostly obtained from the snags they fell at dozens of campgrounds following the tragedy at Riverside Campground.

Well stocked with firewood for the winter, Joe needed to determine how he would survive economically now while laid off from the Forest Service until spring. He applied for temporary positions at the Stevens Pass and Mission Ridge ski areas but hadn't heard back. He subsequently filed for unemployment insurance and mapped out a plan to supplement his income by freelancing articles for magazines and newspapers in the Pacific Northwest.

Having spent time up the Chiwawa River basin as the district's wilderness ranger, Joe had become fascinated with the story of the Trinity mine at the end of the Chiwawa Road at the entrance to the Glacier Peak Wilderness. Trinity, an abandoned mining community, had recently become listed for sale by its owners, Two Rivers Construction. Its future seemed as uncertain as its mysterious past when over three hundred residents had hopes of striking it rich.

Joe researched the story and interviewed several surviving old-timers who had worked at the Trinity mine. With his interviews completed, Joe sent a letter to *Pacific Northwest Magazine* to inquire if the editors might be interested in the story of Trinity.

A week later, Joe received a letter from the editor, John Blazek. "Thank you for your query, Mr. Blanco. Your story idea interests us greatly. We feel your story would be perfect for our December issue. We will remit $250 to you now, with another $250 once you complete the story." Elated, Joe wrote back immediately, accepting their offer and agreeing to meet the deadline.

This is great! Joe thought. *A story in a prestigious magazine like Pacific Northwest Magazine. This story will practically write itself.*

Two weeks later, Joe submitted the article, which ran in the December issue as the cover story featuring original art and the headline: "Ghost Town for Sale," by Joe Blanco. The story read as follows:

> *The American West virtually abounds with ghost towns, old mining communities that began with a prospector's cry of "eureka." For a while, these boom towns flourished, then died—sometimes for strange and mysterious reasons. Such is the case of Trinity, an old mining community approximately 50 miles north of Leavenworth, Washington, in the rugged North Cascades of Washington.*
>
> *Trinity, located at the end of the twenty-five-mile Chiwawa River Road, is now merely a remnant of what it once was. As late as 1930, Trinity was home for more than three hundred men and women employed by the Royal Development Company of New York. Streets in the small boomtown would bustle with bawdy excitement when miners returned after a long day in the mine. Saloons and brothels all awaited the weary miners, providing an enjoyable, though expensive, way to relax after a hard day's work.*
>
> *Today, however, Trinity has been reclaimed for the most part by Mother Nature, who dumps an average of fourteen feet of snow on the townsite annually. Later destroyed by fire and crushed by heavy snows, most of the original thirty-eight buildings are gone. All that remains are a few residences and the generator plant. The town had decayed since the last serious attempt at mining the Trinity claims. But at one time, the residents of Trinity had high hopes of "striking it rich."*

What happened? Why did the mine suddenly shut down with no forewarning in late 1931 on orders from the Royal Development Company headquartered in New York? The reasons, though not altogether clear, were recalled by several former Trinity residents now living at Lake Wenatchee, Plain, Leavenworth, and Seattle. Today in their seventies and eighties, these old-timers reminisced about days of hope and human stamina, despair and drunkenness, and finally, corruption and collapse at the Trinity townsite.

Mildred Naughten of Lake Wenatchee had gone to Trinity in 1929 as a newlywed bride, leaving a legal secretary's job in Wenatchee to marry Jim Naughten, the chief engineer. The winter in Trinity essentially began in late October when heavy snows closed the only road to the outside world.

Naughten, one of only five women at Trinity in those days, said that she and her husband were excited about the prospect of mining vast deposits of silver, copper, and gold in the mine their first year. Besides reports of "solid" veins of ore, she said that the Royal Development Company had provided investors with "unique protection" for their investment.

"The company was uniquely financed," Naughten said. "When an investor deposited a dollar, a matching dollar was put in the Chase National Bank in New York. They had over a million dollars in that bank." In other words, she said the company guaranteed its stockholders their capital stock if the credit of the government was maintained.

So, the Royal Development Company had adequate funds to proceed with their building plans and assay research in the spring of 1930. However, the mine workers were under contract to the company, which had promised to pay their workers based on the total tonnage produced by the mine. Until then, no significant amounts of ore had been produced, according to Bill Burgess, eighty-five, of Lake Wenatchee.

Burgess, a young miner in the early days of Trinity, said the tunnel had been built "solely on speculation." The investors were protected but the miners weren't in the event that the mine didn't pan out, he said.

But the miners' hopes were high, based on the continued investment and interest shown by the Royal Development Company, which claimed that the Trinity site would be "one mine in which no money was lost," claimed Naughten.

"This optimism was accentuated by the fact that the Roman Catholic Church in New York had, in part, financed the mine," explained Naughten. 'That's why the mine was called Trinity."

Naughten said there was good cause for optimism at the townsite in those days. Business was booming despite the Great Depression. Many new buildings, including a mess hall, sawmill, and residences were constructed, along with several more planned for the following summer.

"By 1931, the miners were working day and night to get a shipment of copper ore over to Tacoma for refinement to prove the project would be fruitful," she said.

Then, one autumn night, the fateful news came across the wire from New York. The Royal Development Company had ordered the Trinity mine closed. They gave no explanation for the closure.

Naughten explained, "Most of the miners, immigrants from Eastern Europe, had recently arrived at Trinity, which was twenty-four miles from the nearest good road at Lake Wenatchee. They had spent what little money they had stocking up on groceries for a snowbound six-month winter of expected work. Suddenly, they were out of a job, and they were mad—real mad."

"That night, they opened their kegs of wine and started drinking," Naughten remembered. "A group of immigrants soon became a howling mob, violently angry because the main office had closed the mine for what the miners perceived

as a phony financial reason rather than a lack of ore. The miners went on a rampage, breaking windows and destroying property."

John Hendrickson of Leavenworth, seventy-eight, was one of the miners making four dollars and twenty cents a day when the mine shut down that night in 1931. He remembers the angry crowd of miners as "unruly."

"All of them had their wine," he said. "Liquor was a precious commodity in this remote community," he added. One man, attempting to bring in a case of whiskey through deep winter snows, got lost, and died in the woods.

"They didn't find his body until spring," recalled Hendrickson.

Neither Hendrickson nor Naughten believed the claim that the company went bankrupt from a lack of ore.

"This really was a struggle between those who were operating the mine and those who were financing the mine," Naughten claimed. "The financiers, all Easterners, could care less about the mine. All the investors wanted was to get hold of the money invested in the Chase National Bank."

"The reason they closed so suddenly was that they didn't want proof that there was mineral content enough to make the thing feasible," she continued. "So, the financiers wanted to keep the miners from shipping a carload of ore to the Tacoma Smelter."

"These men had worked overtime to get some truckloads of the stuff ready to transport and the heads of the company did not want this kind of success to happen," added Naughten. "They didn't want to show the mine was profitable so they could get the one million dollars." This undercurrent was sensed by the angry miners, she recounted, so they took it out on the company.

"I guess they took their vengeance out by smashing buildings," she said. "It was a really frightening experience—the noise and the uncertainty of what was going to happen. You

just don't know how far an angry mob will go under these circumstances. The fellows in charge were trying to cope with all this—trying to calm them down. It was sickening news for people who had been up there since 1923 to suddenly have the work stopped."

Naughten said the situation was intensified by rumors the miners were betrayed by one of their own. "The miners felt that someone in the local office was transmitting information back East as to when the shipment would be transported to the smelter," she said. "The men suspected who it was, but the nearest it came to any trouble was when they started talking about tar and feathering this guy."

A.J. Kennedy, an eighty-six-year-old Seattle resident, was head bookkeeper at the Trinity mine when the development folded. Fortunately for him, he happened to be on his honeymoon in the San Juan Islands the night that the mine shut down, he said, and that he wasn't aware of the impending disaster within the company.

"It had been a big building year for the townsite in 1931," Kennedy said. "After the mine shut down, I couldn't buy a job because of the economic depression."

Hendrickson, formerly a consultant to the federal Bureau of Mines, believes that the Royal Development Company "never gave the mine a chance to prove it could be a producer. The Trinity mine is practically solid ore in places," Hendrickson added.

No serious attempt has been made at mining the Trinity tunnel since then, however. The buildings that remain are grim reminders of the Royal Development Company's aborted investment. The Trinity townsite had cycled through several owners since 1931, all content with enjoying their property as a recreational retreat.

Trinity, which sits in the shadow of the 8,500 foot Buck Mountain and other spectacular peaks at the headwaters of the Chiwawa River, is once again for sale, according to owner Don Booth. He said that several mining companies, recreational outfits, and church groups are interested in purchasing the site.

But a lot of unanswered questions remain about the old Trinity mine. Who ordered the mine closed and did they make off with the money deposited in the Chase National Bank? And more importantly, why did the company back out of what appeared to be a fail-proof investment?

"We'll probably never know," conceded Naughten.

Blazek and the other editors at *Pacific Northwest Magazine* loved the article and offered Joe a job as a correspondent covering topics of interest from North Central Washington. Joe also picked up other assignments as a freelancer for *The Oregonian* and the *Seattle Times* and worked as the upper valley correspondent for the *Wenatchee World*. Collectively, it appeared he would survive the winter after all.

As a career urban dweller, Joe would have a unique winter—a Thoreau-like experience in the remote environs of Lake Wenatchee. Hunkered down in the Mushroom Haus, a simple cabin lacking running water and other amenities, Joe would walk or drive to the Lake Wenatchee Ranger Station daily to pick up his mail, shower in the bunkhouse, and dump his garbage.

Creature comforts at the Mushroom Haus were modest: a nineteen-inch black-and-white television, a combination reel-to-reel cassette, and an eight-track tape player, along with an AM-FM radio. Due to its unusual mountain location, Joe had access to only two television stations, but he picked up radio station KZAM-FM, the closest thing to his favorite album-oriented rock station in Portland.

With constant snowfall throughout the winter, Joe came to truly appreciate the solitude of living alone in a mountain cabin. Occasionally, it would snow for twenty-four hours straight, accumulating up to three feet on the ground. One storm literally buried the Mushroom Haus and Joe's truck in the driveway.

But when it snowed, the neighborhood was so muted that it seemed as if the Earth had stopped. Joe loved the peace and quiet of a good snowstorm.

On a particularly cold January night, when the temperature dipped down to thirty-five degrees below zero, Joe was working on a story for the *Wenatchee World*. Taking a break, he sent Kerry a postcard to let him know about his good fortune.

In late January, Joe received a letter in response from Kerry:

Doctah Gonzo:

Wie geht es einen, Herr Doctah? Ich bin gut, hier. Yah, shure!

So good to hear from you, mein freund. It is midpoint in the winter season before we must return to the great forest once again. We must prepare a sacrifice before we begin our summer's work. Have you any ideas of a ceremonial nature?

I have one! The weekend of February 25-26 is a truly cosmic event. I will journey to the Mushroom Haus on February 25. From there, we must travel to Frenchman Coulee south of Wenatchee and prepare for the total solar eclipse scheduled to occur at 8:22 a.m. on Monday, February 26. What do you say to that, Herr Doctah?

I will have a small caravan with me—nothing out of the ordinary: several women, herd animals, food, wine, and spiritual refreshments. I hope all is well at Lake Wenatchee. Please send my greetings to one and all. May the force be with you. We shall have a great season!

Happy trails, Dr. Gonzo.

Love, Kerry.

On February 23, it started snowing and didn't stop until the evening of February 25. By then, more than forty-eight inches of snow had accumulated in a forty-eight-hour period.

As Joe was calling it a night, he flipped off the television. Then he noticed how eerily hushed it was inside the Mushroom Haus. Joe understood the science behind the silence. The snow absorbs many of the sound waves, causing the muffled calm outside. With virtually no traffic at the end of Highway 207, it seemed deathly quiet outside.

Just then, a knock on the back door rattled the silence, sending a start through Joe's system. Kerry had arrived at the Mushroom Haus.

"Jesus, mein herring, you scared the bejeepers out of me!" said Joe.

"Sorry, herring," replied Kerry. "Are you ready for a trip to Frenchman Coulee for the total solar eclipse?"

"Yes, when my blood pressure retreats to its normal parameters," responded Joe.

"To make it interesting," continued Kerry, "I have procured some psilocybin just for the occasion. I also have the antidote, some very strong weed."

"I could use a little of the weed right now," confessed Joe.

Frenchman Coulee north of Vantage, Washington

That night, they shoveled the driveway, cleared the wraparound deck on the Mushroom Haus, and prepared for their sojourn to

Frenchman Coulee in the Columbia Basin to witness the rare occasion of a total solar eclipse.

Early the next morning, Kerry and Joe ate mushrooms and drove to Frenchman Coulee with their camera equipment in tow. At the appointed time, they witnessed the total solar eclipse in a surreal natural environment.

In March, Joe received another letter from Kerry, who was apparently taking a break from his studies:

Mein herring:

Ah, decisions, decisions. I must decide by this evening if I go on a ten-day ski tour of the Pasayten Wilderness or a trip to the Grand Canyon. There are no omens this time. I must decide without consulting the orb. I will go into my chambers now—bring the girl!

If I venture to the Grand Canyon, I will not be back until April 1. Spring quarter begins April 2, However, if I go to the Pasayten Wilderness, I will be back on March 25. Then I would have time for a stop at the Mushroom Haus for a visit. Could you give the key to Carli if you happen to be out of town?

Ah, mein herring, if you are claiming the upper Chiwawa realm of the Glacier Peak Wilderness this summer, I must have the upper White and Napeequa River basins. The other wild and crazy wilderness strangers can patrol the Little Wenatchee and Alpine Lakes. We will hold summit meetings once again in the Napeequa.

I'll call the ranger station on Friday, March 16, and leave a message with Carli. If I go to the Grand Canyon on March 22, I will probably arrive for a summit meeting this coming weekend. See Carli for details.

Happy trails, Helmut Vallindaklopf.

P.S. Return der Wald to the beasts.

Before mailing his latest missive, Kerry wrote another letter on the back of the same piece of paper.

> *Ah, mein herring, I found this letter in the bottom of my truck—quite outdated! The Pasayten trip was glorious—ten days of sunshine and daydreaming in the powder snow. Now it's back to life at the university—always the university. I will pass through Lake Wenatchee soon. I will be helping a friend move from Wenatchee to Bellingham, so we'll stop by. Her name is Kimberly. She is my new girlfriend.*
>
> *Who will be in the Mushroom Haus this summer? Can I stay there with you? How about the trailers or other abodes? I must have a stereo and books and a place to "entertain" guests this summer. Keep an eye out for me, Herr Doktor. I will see you soon.*
>
> *Love, Vallindaklopf*

By April, Joe was back in the clear-cuts of the Lake Wenatchee Ranger District leading a crew of tree planters in reforesting treeless logging sites. One day, he put pen to paper and shipped off a letter to Kerry:

> *Mein herring, I have two bits of good news for you. First of all, Rachael has been hired as a prevention guard in the district. She will be living in the Rock Creek Guard Station up the Chiwawa, so I will be staying with her most of the time. That means you can bunk at the Mushroom Haus if you like.*
>
> *Really enjoyed our junket to Frenchman Coulee for the solar eclipse, and I have some stunning photos for you to review. I continue to make a tolerable living from my freelance career and have been hired as the North Central Washington correspondent for the Oregonian, no less.*
>
> *You'll love my latest feature on the hard freeze affecting the fruits orchards in the Wenatchee Valley. I describe my*

sources—the professionals working at the Washington State University Tree Fruit Research and Extension Center—as "fruit scientists."

I imagine we'll have fun with that one this summer. Looking forward to your arrival.

Ciao, Joe

CHAPTER FOURTEEN

Package from Spiderman

Kerry arrived at the Mushroom Haus right before the annual wilderness ranger training, which this summer was slated at Eightmile Lake on the Leavenworth Ranger District. The cast of characters would now include Hannah Murray, the new lead wilderness ranger, and Lutkea Finnes, who had worked on the fire crew the previous season.

A few days after the wilderness training, Kerry burst into the Mushroom Haus, alarmed and shaken.

"One of the lads on the fire crew just told me that they were holding a package sent to me at the ranger station," he said, gasping for air. "The return address only says 'Spiderman.'"

"What do you mean 'holding,' mein herring?" inquired Joe.

"A friend from Hawaii just sent me a package," responded Kerry, collecting himself. "It's marked 'hold for surveillance' by the post office and it's sitting on the ranger's desk."

"Relax, herring," said Joe, assuredly. "What's in the package?"

"I think it's a quantity of psilocybin," said Kerry.

"Let's go," suggested Joe without hesitation. "The ranger station is closed."

Though Kerry was a risk-taker, Joe was bold in ways that his friend was not; he used his Forest Service key to access the building. Sure enough, the package on the ranger's desk was clearly marked "hold for surveillance." Joe filched the package right off the ranger's desk, and the pair retreated to the Mushroom Haus.

"Holy shit!" exclaimed Kerry. "There's a whole summer's supply of Hawaiian mushrooms here."

"Excellent!" said Joe. "This Mushroom Haus will become a double entendre."

This season, the wilderness rangers would also monitor the high routes, many of which hadn't received attention for years. These routes were becoming increasingly popular with weekend climbers and bow hunters.

On their first reconnaissance mission on a climbing route, the Aldo Leopold Society ate some of Kerry's mushrooms and targeted the Leroy-Chipmunk-Carne High Route at the base of Seven-Fingered Jack.

Hiking to Leroy Creek from the Phelps Creek Trailhead, Joe noticed the wildflowers: "Wow, the variety of color here is remarkable."

"That's the mushrooms talking, mein herring," said Kerry. It was true. Under the influence of Hawaiian mushrooms, the colors were even more vivid.

"And the smell of the mountain wildflowers," continued Joe. "I smell slide alder and western anemone," added Joe. After camping in Leroy Basin for the night, the rangers climbed Seven-Fingered Jack.

At this altitude, the humongous deer flies became an issue. The flies swarmed and relentlessly ricocheted off the rangers, who were well covered with hats and bandanas to protect themselves from the buzzing pests.

"Can you believe these kamikaze deer flies?" asked Kerry.

"Oh, yes," responded Joe. "As trail dogs, we hiked with stock animals. They were natural targets, so we learned to be prepared."

As they ascended the southwest ridge of Seven-Fingered Jack, a strong easterly wind picked up and the deer flies magically disappeared.

"Wow, what a view!" exclaimed Gottlieb, peering down onto Entiat Glacier.

The sheer cliff on the north side of the mountain took their breath away. "That would be a long drop before you even landed," added the Dogman.

Resting on the sunny and warm summit, they broke for lunch and marveled at the panorama of the North Cascades. After lunch, they skirted down the ridge along Chipmunk Creek to Carne Basin and then dropped down the Carne Mountain Trail to their original starting point at the Phelps Creek Trailhead.

Lead Wilderness Ranger Hannah Murray organized the next trip. This one would focus on replanting denuded campsites due to overuse near two popular lakes. Joe, Kerry, and Lutkea Finnes departed the ranger station first thing in the morning. Hannah, consigned to paperwork in the office, would rendezvous with the team in the early afternoon at Top Lake, about a half-mile from Pear Lake.

After a pit stop at the Mushroom Haus for some mushrooms on their way to the Top Lake Trailhead, the trio consumed the psilocybin at the trailhead and started hiking. By the time they reached the crest of the ridge over Top Lake, they were wired.

"Let's stop for a break," suggested Joe.

"Sounds good," said Lutkea.

"What say we pop a bottle of wine?" suggested Kerry. The others nodded enthusiastically.

"Maybe it will help temper the increasing intensity of these mushrooms," said Joe.

After finishing the bottle in short order, the threesome proceeded down the trail to Top Lake. Suddenly overcome with a burst of ardor, Lutkea peeled off her ranger uniform and dove into Top Lake, buck-ass naked. Joe and Kerry, shocked by her bit of derring-do, also stripped their clothes off and dove into the warm, shallow mountain lake.

After a few minutes, the three rangers could hear Hannah coming down the trail above Top Lake, calling, "Yoo-hoo! Where are you kids?"

Surprised by the timing of Hannah's arrival, the three rangers nonetheless continued swimming. Lutkea and Kerry had no qualms about skinny dipping. Joe, on the other hand, was a tad self-conscious. When Hannah arrived at the lake's edge, Lutkea implored Hannah to join them.

Top Lake from the west

"No thanks, Lutkea," Hannah replied. "I'll just wait until you kids are done having your fun."

Once they toweled off and put their uniforms back on, the group proceeded to Pear Lake, where they rendezvoused with Mary Banta, the district's wildlife technician. Before pitching their tents, they spent the rest of the day revegetating the denuded areas around Pear Lake.

At the end of the workday, Kerry and Joe—still wired on mushrooms—packed their fishing poles over the ridge above Pear Lake to Peach Lake, a little-used fishing hole off the beaten path. The trout were biting, so they packed what they caught back to camp. They cleaned the fish, breaded the outsides, and fried them in olive oil. Kerry also steamed some broccoli and carrots.

"Yumm, this meal is delicious!" said Mary.

"I agree," added Hannah. "Kerry, you're quite the backcountry connoisseur."

Joe, not to be outdone, announced, "Wait until all of you try my macaroni and cheese with Spam." Everybody laughed heartily as they enjoyed their meal.

Still wired after dark, Kerry and Joe adjourned to their tent. With headlamps on, they spent the night waxing philosophical, discussing existentialism, religion, epistemology, logic, and metaphysics. While Joe and Kerry agreed on a wide spectrum of subjects, they appeared to have differences of opinion on some issues.

Kerry subscribed to the teachings of Epicurus, the Greek philosopher and sage whose primary focus was determining how to live the best possible life. "Joy is vital" he would tell Joe. Kerry did not believe in an afterlife. Joe, however, wasn't ready to rule out the possibility.

Kerry would often reflect on the nature of his own demise. For example, he admired his sister's husband who, when stricken with cancer, committed suicide. Kerry also had an unhealthy admiration for Ernest Hemingway, telling Joe that "when the time comes, I'll be checking out on my own terms."

Joe, on the other hand, had a different perspective. He was a realist, much like Aristotle and Plato. Joe's mantra was "most things in moderation," and his philosophy was to find the middle ground for an all-around better life. His ultimate goal was to have kids and live a long life.

"Kerry, you must understand, I would rather suffer to the end of my corporeal life rather than risk losing my eternal soul," pronounced Joe.

Joe and Kerry simply agreed to disagree on the concept of an afterlife, yet they concurred on living life to the fullest. Continuing their discussion into the wee hours, Kerry said he diverted from Epicurus when it came to one subject: old age.

"When I have exhausted my sense of adventure and have lost the excitement of living, I don't see much sense in continuing on," Kerry said. "I can't see myself wheeling around a nursing home, dribbling soup down the front of my robe."

"Geez, Kerry, you're such a pessimist," countered Joe. "When you're young, so much of what we do is difficult. We're constantly in the process of finding our way: going to school, seeking employment, starting a family. You're always in a state of striving."

"But when you've reached a certain age, you can just sit by the campfire, reflect, and truly appreciate life with no more pressure," Joe continued. "You can play with your grandchildren, enjoy visiting friends, travel widely, listen to music, and muse on the stories of our lives."

Finally, after more mushroom-fueled discussion, Kerry and Joe fell asleep just before dawn. A short while later, Hannah's sweet voice called out.

"Yoo-hoo, boys, it's time to get cracking!" she said with her characteristic enthusiasm. "We need to finish our revegetation project here at Pear Lake and then do the same at Top Lake on our way out."

"Shit," mumbled Joe. "I haven't had enough sleep. What will we do, mein herring?"

"I have the solution," replied Kerry, as he plucked a baggie from his backpack. "More Hawaiian mushrooms."

"Excellent idea," responded Joe. "A little pinch between the cheek and gum, followed by a cup of strong coffee, and we're on our way."

"Precisely," nodded Kerry.

"Good thing the weekend is near," added Joe. "When we return to the Mushroom Haus, I'm going to sleep for twenty-four hours straight."

CHAPTER FIFTEEN

Fire on the Mountain

Recovering from their Pear Lake excursion, Kerry and Joe knew it was time to plan their next junket.

As Kerry was fond of saying, "If it's not on the calendar, it's not happening."

Kerry and Joe had agreed to a bold venture: hike the entire length of the Icicle Ridge Trail from Stevens Pass to Leavenworth, a forty-four-mile trek through the Alpine Lakes Wilderness Area. Along the way, they would rendezvous with Chaz Marley, one of the Leavenworth Ranger District wilderness guards, at Lake Augusta. Together, they would then climb Big Jim Mountain.

Big Jim Mountain from Hatchery Creek

Big Jim Mountain was one of two peaks in the area named after James J. Hill, the visionary "robber baron" and builder of the Great Northern Railway. In an age that witnessed the likes of J.P. Morgan, John D. Rockefeller, Jay Gould, and Andrew Carnegie, James J. Hill more than held his own with that group. His goal was to build a railroad from Minneapolis to Seattle over the daunting North Cascades of Washington. Despite numerous setbacks, Hill eventually pulled it off, establishing a transcontinental route along the northern latitudes of the United States.

By far the biggest catastrophe in the early days of Hill's "Empire Builder" occurred in 1910, when a massive blizzard hit near the tiny town of Wellington just west of Stevens Pass. For nine days at the end of February, the Wellington area was blitzed with a severe blizzard.

On the worst day, eleven feet of snow fell. Near the end of the storm, two trains bound from Spokane to Seattle, a passenger train and a mail train, were trapped in the Wellington depot. Even snowplows couldn't penetrate the repeated avalanches and resulting snow accumulation along that stretch of tracks.

Then, on February 28, the snowfall stopped and was followed by rain and a warm wind. Early the next morning, a huge slab of snow broke loose from the side of Windy Mountain because of a lightning strike. A ten-foot wall of snow, half a mile long and a quarter-mile wide, descended the steep hillside toward the town. A forest fire had recently ravaged the slopes above Wellington, leaving few obstacles to slow down the avalanche, which squarely hit the railroad depot.

Most of the passengers and crew were asleep at the time when the impact sent the trains careening more than one hundred and fifty feet into the valley below. Ninety-six people were killed; survivors were pulled from the wreckage by railroad employees who had immediately rushed from the hotel and other buildings. The Wellington avalanche was the deadliest in the history of the United States. En route to Stevens Pass, Kerry and Joe visited the site of the Wellington disaster before departing for their trek from Stevens Pass to Leavenworth.

The Icicle Ridge Trail runs east-west from subalpine terrain on the crest of the Cascades to the drier, pine-inhabited lowlands of the Wenatchee Valley. Listed in the guidebooks as "strenuous," the first fifteen miles are designated as "unmaintained," meaning the trail becomes brushier and harder to follow.

From Stevens Pass, Kerry and Joe hiked south for a few miles past Lake Susan Jane before the trail turned in an easterly direction from Lake Josephine, the headwaters of the Icicle River. At Lake Josephine, Joe sprained his ankle and his pace slowed considerably, but Kerry was intent on arriving at Doelle Lakes by dark.

"Mein herring," said Kerry, "you catch up when you can. I'm going to blast by Chain Lakes and head over the ridge near Bull's Tooth Mountain to Doelle Lakes."

"I'll see you on the other side of the pass," he added.

Joe soldiered on but continued to struggle with his swollen ankle. With a decidedly steep turn up toward Chain Lakes, the brutal grade of the trail exacted a further toll. Joe lost his footing and took a spill, resulting in a massive cut and nasty contusions on his left kneecap. Struggling ever so slowly up the trail, Joe arrived at Chain Lakes, bleeding and in considerable pain. He patched his knee with supplies from his first aid kit to stop the bleeding.

Arriving at Chain Lakes, Joe searched for signs of Kerry, but he was nowhere to be found. Joe assumed Kerry had continued to their planned destination at Upper Doelle Lake. But daylight was waning, and Joe could go no further. He was done for the day. Concerned about bears, Joe camped near another couple hiking with two Labrador retrievers. Canines are always a deterrent for *Ursus americanus*. Joe then set up his tent, rolled out his sleeping bag, and quickly drifted into slumberland.

The next morning, Joe woke before dawn, refreshed and feeling remarkably chipper. Determined to catch up with Kerry and knowing that his friend was a late sleeper, he broke camp and headed up the trail toward the pass adjacent to Bull's Tooth, a peak that dominated the skyline at 6,800 feet.

Reaching the pass at sunrise, Joe was rewarded with stunning views of Glacier Peak to the north and Mt. Hinman to the south. Spotting Kerry's tent below the pass next to Upper Doelle Lake, Joe signaled his arrival.

Doelle Lake on Icicle Ridge

Joe began. "Mein herring, I had an accident coming up the trail to Chain Lakes. I punctured my knee with a sharp, pointy root on the trail when I dropped to avoid slipping down the hillside."

"Are you okay?" asked Kerry.

"Yes," Joe responded, "but I wasn't able to catch up, so I stayed at Chain Lakes last night."

Knowing that the next stretch of the Icicle Ridge Trail would be tricky, the twosome continued. The map indicated the next section was "not maintained."

"More like nonexistent," said Kerry, as they immediately lost the trail.

Unsure which direction to proceed and after scouring the terrain around Lower Doelle Lake for a trail, they were ready to give up. Just then, a couple of hikers approached from the direction of Frosty Pass.

"We're trying to get to Frosty Pass," said Joe, "but the trail is tough to find."

"Good luck," the woman warned. "We gave up."

The two rangers momentarily considered heading back to Stevens Pass until Joe said, "Shit, herring, we can't give up. Let's keep looking."

Undaunted, they muddled ahead. Then inexplicably, Kerry and Joe finally stumbled on what looked like the start of the trail to Frosty Pass.

Now on a solid trail, they came to a meadow that unfolded with a blanket of wildflowers, including western anemone and giant red paintbrush. Elated that they had found the trail, Kerry broke into song: "The hills are alive, with the sound of music...."

"Mein herring, as much as I love the paintbrush, I really love the western anemone," said Joe. "It's hairy, like an animal."

Kerry replied that "as beautiful as they are, paintbrush is technically a parasite. The roots of the paintbrush establish connections with the roots of other species, and they are impossible to transplant or grow by seed."

Deep into the meadow, the trail became increasingly scarce, and eventually, nonexistent. "Shit, we lost the trail again," muttered Kerry.

"Yeah," affirmed Joe, "I can see how those two hikers gave it up."

As skilled as Kerry was in the backcountry, Joe had otherworldly skills when finding trails. "Just watch," Joe told Kerry. "We'll find it again."

Bushwhacking for about a half-mile, they crested a ridge and spotted the well-defined trail leading to Frosty Pass in the distance.

Arriving at Frosty Pass, they had their choice among two high mountain camp spots at Lake Mary and Lake Margaret. A side trail diverged to Lake Margaret, but Lake Mary was right on their trail. Exhausted from the day's journey, Kerry and Joe were thankful when a fellow traveler offered to share his campsite at Lake Mary.

The stunning high mountain lake is framed by Snowgrass Mountain, an eight-thousand-foot peak at the terminus of the Chiwaukum Range intersecting with Icicle Ridge. Once their tents were set up, the pair started a small campfire, pulled out a fifth of vodka, and relaxed for a bit.

"What's the deal with all these lakes named after women?" inquired Kerry.

"Well, that's A.H. Sylvester, a topographer on the Snoqualmie National Forest who eventually became the first Wenatchee National Forest supervisor in the early part of the twentieth century," explained Joe.

"He named thousands of geological features during his time as forest supervisor," said Joe. "Sylvester would travel the forest trails and map many features of the areas. At that time, the forests were mostly unmapped and lacking in topographical names. To better protect the forests from wildfire, Sylvester believed that natural features needed names and detailed maps so that forest fires could be located quickly.

"Sylvester was an 'on-the-ground' type of forest supervisor," Joe continued. "You might say he was the original wilderness ranger on the Wenatchee National Forest, making many first ascents of several mountains. He was the first to roam the Enchantments, perhaps the most spectacular feature in the forest."

"That makes sense," replied Kerry. "How do you know all this?"

"Mein herring," Joe responded, "remember, I've had all that office time to study up on the subject. I was intrigued by all the names of the whimsical features, especially those focusing on Native Americans, early explorers, prospectors, sheepherders, and even family members—both his family and those of many of his backcountry hiking companions."

"Like Mary?" asked Kerry.

"Yep," confirmed Joe. "Mary and Margaret were the sisters of Byrne Canby, Sylvester's hiking companion. We'll see several other lakes named after women on this trip: Florence, Flora, and Ida, to name a few. Tomorrow, we'll traverse Ladies Pass, so I hope the weather improves."

"Sadly, Sylvester died right up there on Snowgrass Mountain," continued Joe. "When he was taking a break, one of his pack horses stumbled and fell, taking him down a steep, rocky slope. Rescuers transported him to a hospital in Wenatchee, but within a week he died of his injuries."

While their fellow traveler was off scouting Ladies Pass before dark, Joe and Kerry noticed a marmot rifling through his gear with gusto. Kerry chased the animal away, but the high-elevation critter soon returned to continue rummaging.

"I've seen many a marmot," said Kerry, "but I've never encountered such an audacious critter as this."

Nineteenth-century miners and trappers called marmots "whistling pigs," due to their high-pitched whistles. Marmots are high-elevation wilderness rodents that look like beavers without the tail. They have very long claws for burrowing tunnels where they hibernate in the high country during the long winters.

The pair took turns chasing the relentless rodent, which was amazingly fleet of foot. They decided to name the varmint "Max, the Mischievous Marmot." At the end of a very long day, they retired after dinner.

The next morning, an "upper-level disturbance" moved into the North Cascades. The day started out rainy and wet, and it only got worse. Packing their camp, Kerry and Joe had no idea what was to come.

"You know what they say, herring," Kerry reminded Joe. "The mountains make their own weather."

While they marched up the switchbacks above Lake Mary, clouds funneled up toward Ladies Pass at an incredible pace, blasting the rangers with a fierce wind and pelting them with hail.

At the pass, they could see lightning strikes in the distance; they hastened their descent to Lake Ida. In upper Index Creek, the foul weather abated a bit. From there, they climbed up to Carter Lake and pitched camp, even though their goal was further on at Lake Augusta. At Carter Lake, they located Leavenworth wilderness ranger, Chaz Marley.

"You're going to have to retreat off Icicle Ridge, gentlemen," Chaz informed Kerry and Joe. "We have a large lightning-caused forest fire further down the ridge. I've been posted here to redirect hikers to detour downward toward either the Icicle River or the Wenatchee River."

"Well, that's a bummer," said Kerry. "Guess that means our climb up Big Jim Mountain is off."

"I'm afraid so, Kerry," said Chaz. "Since you two work at Lake Wenatchee, you might want to hike down Hatchery Creek to US Highway 2."

Before setting up camp, Joe radioed the ranger station and asked for Randy Wilson, the assistant fire management officer.

"Randy, we need your help. Kerry and I are abandoning our trip down Icicle Ridge tomorrow because of the fire down the ridge near Leavenworth," Joe explained. "Could you pick us up at the Hatchery Creek Trailhead tomorrow at four p.m.?"

Randy agreed and said that he would meet them at the parking lot where the Hatchery Creek Trail begins near Tumwater Campground. Joe and Kerry then established camp, cooked dinner, and relaxed with some cider and vodka before calling it a night.

Both rangers were cold and wet, so they changed into dry clothes before retiring. When they did retire, the wind howled, making it difficult to sleep. Later that night, Joe suddenly awoke. His tent was illuminated and no longer flapping in the breeze.

"*It couldn't be morning already,*" Joe thought.

He looked at his watch; it was three a.m. Curious, he peeked outside his tent and saw why it was suddenly calm. The storm had vanished, and a bright full moon drenched the entire basin with light. This was very good news, indeed. It meant summer would return at daybreak.

The next morning, Kerry and Joe packed their camp and hustled down Painter Creek to where the trail skirts a ridge and drops into Hatchery Creek. Much like horses and mules, the soggy rangers were stepping lively, knowing they were "smelling the barn."

CHAPTER SIXTEEN

High Hunt

After Labor Day, the wilderness rangers focused on preparations for the "high hunt," which occurs for a ten-day period starting in mid-September. Primarily for bowhunters and rifle sportsmen pursuing their game in wilderness areas, access is by foot or horseback only. For wilderness rangers, high hunt patrol is not an assignment for the faint of heart.

To prepare, the rangers concentrated on heavy-use areas, installing new Wallowa toilets, and performing other backcountry chores prior to the most popular time of the season, when hunters can pursue their prey and backpackers can hike bug-free.

Digging holes for Wallowa toilets can be damn tough. The soil isn't always so accommodating, with rocks and roots and other obstacles making it nearly impossible to dig. By the time the hole is deep enough, the top of the shovel handle needs to be level with the surface. The job always seems to take longer than it should.

Chiwawa Basin needed a new Wallowa toilet added in the upper portion of the drainage, so Joe, Kerry, and Gottlieb hiked to the upper basin to work on that project, while the Dogman, Hannah, and Mary Wiltz trekked into Carne Basin to install a new toilet in that popular hunting locale.

With plenty of folks to accomplish the tasks at hand, the trip would be quick and enjoyable. The weather was perfect—sunny and warm, with nary a bug. Joe, Kerry, and Gottlieb then hiked over Phelps Ridge, setting up a rendezvous with the Dogman, Hannah, and Mary in Spider Meadows. Hiking out the next day, the camaraderie among the group was palpable.

"I love you guys," announced Kerry sincerely.

He was particularly smitten with Mary. "I need to get to know her better if you know what I mean," Kerry later confided to Joe.

A few days before the start of high hunt, Raoul Stanford would assign locations to assure thorough coverage. At the meeting to divvy up locations, the first topic of discussion was the high-use locations like White River, Spider Meadows, and Buck Creek Pass.

Entiat Range from Spider Glacier

"I prefer the White River area myself," said Kerry, "but anywhere on the east side of Glacier Peak will be slammed with people."

"Okay, Kerry," replied Raoul. "You got it."

"Who wants Spider Meadow?" asked Raoul. "It will be real crowded up there."

The Dogman volunteered, "I'll take Spider Meadow." Gottlieb chose the Little Giant Pass and Upper Napeequa River areas and Lutkea offered to cover the wilderness beyond Little Wenatchee Ford.

"Okay, that leaves the Buck Creek Pass area to Joe," said Raoul. "Last year the trailhead was filled to capacity with hunters using stock animals. Are you up for that, Joe?"

"Absolutely," he replied without hesitation.

"I'll pack you in and help you establish your camp before hiking out," added Raoul, flashing his signature smile.

Raoul was widely recognized as the godfather of the Lake Wenatchee District. As recreation supervisor, he helped establish many new campgrounds and initiated the construction of new trails. He also served as the snow survey ranger and developed many of the district's snowmobile and cross-country ski trail systems.

Literally a jack-of-all-trades, Raoul assisted in implementing various wildlife management activities and assessing cultural sites of the Wenatchi band of the Yakama Nation. With a remarkable work ethic, Raoul truly enjoyed people, loved the outdoors, and always took a nap during the lunch hour.

Most importantly, he was a beloved mentor to his younger colleagues and a friend to one and all. Joe loved spending time with Raoul, who was always ready with a quick smile.

On Thursday, Joe and Raoul departed the ranger station for Trinity, hiking up Buck Creek to the pass. The trail had recently been rerouted away from Buck Creek to allow hikers to avoid the multiple back-and-forth muddy creek crossings due to overuse by stock animals. Not everybody was on board with the change, however. Legendary mountaineer Fred Beckey noted in one of his books that "the unnecessary low-gradient switchbacks add needless distance to the Buck Creek Trail."

Unlike many narrow passes in the Glacier Peak Wilderness, Buck Creek Pass features a broad area with many campsites, along with a large horse camp on the south end of the pass. All campsites offer easy access to water for horsemen and backpackers alike.

During the high hunt, the Buck Creek Pass horse camp would inevitably have a full house, since most hunters use horses and mules to access the wilderness. Raoul and Joe established a camp in a location that offered a strategic view of most of the other sites in the pass.

That evening, ominous clouds from a predicted storm brought rain, dousing whatever black flies remained in the vicinity. The storm was brief, and the sun reappeared for the remainder of the day.

"Back in my day, wool was the clothing of choice for dealing with nasty weather," said Raoul. "Wool would keep you warm even when wet."

"True," agreed Joe, "but today, quick-drying synthetics are now the rage in the backcountry. They're super light and easy to store in your backpack. But I must confess that I did bring along a wool sweater."

Raoul smiled broadly.

The next day, Raoul and Joe surveyed the pass for activity, though only a few hunters had established camps so far. The big rush would come on Saturday when horsemen would roll up the trail en masse for opening day. High hunt is a short season, with only a ten-day window. Most stay only long enough to accomplish their task of bagging a buck.

Raoul and Joe hiked to the top of the pass to see the spectacular views of Fortress Mountain and Buck Mountain. However, the most compelling view from Buck Creek Pass was the one of Glacier Peak, one of the largest stratovolcanoes in the Cascade Range.

At 10,451 feet, Glacier Peak—known as Dakobed to the Sauk-Suiattle tribes who lived in the vicinity—may not be familiar to many alpine enthusiasts. Surrounded by wilderness and named for its many glaciers, the mountain provides no easy access. Hikers must trek many miles through extremely rough terrain to reach the mountain. Surrounded by deep valleys, cliffs, and ramparts of ice, the mountain is familiar only to those willing to strive for it.

On this day, Raoul and Joe sat in the sun on a couple of flat rocks at the top of Buck Creek Pass and absorbed the compelling view.

"Well, Joe, it's time for me to head down the trail," said Raoul as he hoisted his pack. "I have a lot of work at home this late in the season in terms of getting in the hay. Good luck to you for the next ten days."

Glacier Peak from Buck Creek Pass

"Thanks for accompanying me, Raoul," replied Joe.

By morning, clouds had enveloped the pass, and it started to rain—light at first, then harder. Joe patrolled the area as hunters started arriving, checking their wilderness permits. But it was wet and getting wetter by the minute. By noon, Joe was soaked to the skin.

Before returning to his camp, he checked the horse camp at the base of Liberty Cap. There he noticed an unusually large sheepherder's tent with hobbled horses grazing nearby, so he decided to check in with the group.

"Anybody home?" Joe announced outside the tent.

"Come on in," came the response. Entering the large wall tent, Joe was greeted by a grizzled-looking fellow. "Hi, I'm Brandon Klum. I'm the game warden in these parts. Welcome!"

Pleased with the warm welcome, Joe introduced himself: "Hi, I'm Joe Blanco, wilderness ranger on the Lake Wenatchee Ranger

District. Pleased to meet you. Man, it's nice and warm in here. I'm freezing."

"Joe, these other two soggy sons-of-bitches are Mike Ryan and Jim Cone from our office in Wenatchee," Brandon said. "Would you like to stay a while and dry off?"

"That would be great!" Joe replied.

For various reasons, Joe was relieved to see game wardens in the vicinity. For one thing, game wardens are fully commissioned peace officers, just like state police. Joe was feeling reassured. Game wardens carry firearms and are fully capable of using them if necessary. He would leave whatever law enforcement duties were necessary during the high hunt to them. Plus, they had a woodstove in their spacious tent, and it was warm.

"You want a cup of 'cowboy punch'?" asked Brandon.

"Sure, what is it?" Joe responded.

"Basically, it's lemonade mix and water with a couple shots of vodka," replied Brandon.

"Sounds great," said Joe.

"Pull up a chair," said Brandon. "We're just tuning in the game on our radio."

On this day, the University of Washington Huskies were playing the University of Oregon Ducks in a rivalry football game, and the reception from the Seattle-area radio station at Buck Creek Pass was clear as can be.

"You a Husky fan?" asked Brandon.

"Well, no," replied Joe, rather sheepishly. "Actually, I graduated from Oregon."

"Don't worry, we won't kick you out," said Brandon. "You're welcome to stay."

Thank goodness, Joe thought. *It's warm in here and this punch tastes good.*

The Huskies were the twelfth-ranked team in the country. They would likely have little problem with the lowly Ducks. But the University of Oregon was fired up for the game and it turned into an exciting contest. The Huskies eventually squeaked by the Ducks, 21–17.

"Your boys did okay today, Joe," commented Brandon.

"Yes, they did," said Joe, feeling like the game was a moral victory for the Ducks.

After the game, the musical programming returned on the album-oriented rock station. The first song played was "Francine" by ZZ Top.

"There's my boy, Billy Gibbons," announced Brandon.

"Yeah, I love ZZ Top too," said Joe.

"Billy's actually my cousin," replied Brandon.

"You're shitting me. Really?" asked Joe.

"Really, really," said Brandon. "I see him every year when I visit my parents down in Texas."

After another drink, Joe thanked his hosts and returned to his tent.

For the rest of the high hunt, the weather was miserable. At higher elevations, it snowed. Hunters love it when it snows because they can track the footprints of their prospective prey. At Buck Creek Pass, it just rained, sometimes hard, sometimes just mist. Joe huddled in his tent inside his sleeping bag, reading his book by headlamp.

Earlier in the summer, Joe tasked himself with reading both the Old Testament and the New Testament in his off-hours—not exactly light reading. Growing up Catholic, Joe had already read both books as a child in religion class. Yet, for some odd reason, he wanted to read the entire Bible again, this time from an adult's perspective. The books and many of the stories took on new meanings.

During the high hunt, however, Joe was on to more enjoyable tomes, starting with *On the Road* by Jack Kerouac. Joe dreamed of taking a road trip of his own to find America, searching for adventure. Preoccupied with college and exploring the wilderness, Joe was ready for a different type of experience—a road trip. Unknowingly, Joe would soon find himself on the road.

At the end of September, with high hunt over, it was time for the Aldo Leopold Society to scour the backcountry for a season's worth of garbage left by hunters and other visitors to the Glacier Peak and Alpine Lakes Wilderness areas. Raoul assigned Joe to patrol the entire Pacific Crest Trail on the Lake Wenatchee District for a week, proceeding north from Stevens Pass to White Pass to haul what trash he could carry out of the wilderness.

"Plan on bringing the mules," said Raoul. "We'll use the stock truck, and I'll drop you off and pick you up."

"Sounds good. May I bring Rachael along on this trek?" Joe asked Raoul.

"Certainly, she could help a lot," Raoul said approvingly.

"Thanks, Raoul," Joe replied.

Joe started his trek at Stevens Pass with two stock animals—Pancake, a mule, and Jimmy, a burro. He spent the next two days hiking the PCT to Cady Pass, where he rendezvoused with Rachael. This was Joe's first solo trip with the stock animals, but by now he had become a grizzled veteran when it came to wrangling horses and mules.

Pancake, the wily one, was much smarter than Jimmy. Pancake could finagle his way out of hobbles and create all kinds of mischief when inspired. Joe hadn't forgotten how many times Pancake ran away at the end of a long day.

On one such occasion. Fergie and Joe were preparing their camp at Lake Ethel when Pancake inexplicably took off, sprinting the entire three miles down to the trailhead. Joe and Fergie had no choice but to run down the trail and bring him back. Jimmy wasn't as bold as Pancake, but he could create his own difficulties at creek crossings because he was skittish and spooked easily.

Joe's first day on the PCT went smoothly with the animals. He camped at Lake Janus for the night, where there was plenty of grass for Pancake and Jimmy. Meeting up at Cady Pass the next day, Joe and Rachael continued to Lake Sally Ann where they established their camp for the evening.

A small but beautiful pond, Lake Sally Ann is tucked in a cirque adjacent to the PCT. The Wallowa toilet provided nearby is located on a ridge with compelling views of Mt. Rainier, Mt. Stuart, and the Wenatchee Mountains.

"This is by far the best toilet view on the entire Wenatchee National Forest," Joe informed Rachael.

After two more days on the PCT, Joe and Rachael had collected everything from metal to plastic left by campers during the high hunt. Exiting the PCT at White Pass, Joe and Rachael initiated the long trek down the White River, camping for the night at Lightning Creek before reaching the trailhead. Always punctual, Raoul was waiting with the stock truck.

"Looks like you picked up a lot of garbage," commented Raoul.

"Yes, indeed, so it was well worth the trip," replied Joe. "I'll bet we can fill the back of a pickup truck. Good thing you brought the one ton."

As the summer weather diminished, port season returned, and change was nigh. The foul stench of weirdness—portending all sorts of unsettling events in the forms of sudden changes, revelations, and bad juju—wafted in the air.

The legend of the Mushroom Haus had grown to epic proportions, and some management types who worked at the Lake Wenatchee Ranger District weren't happy about it. A popular hangout for seasonal employees, the Mushroom Haus had become well known for its dubious reputation as a party hub and a den of iniquity.

By the end of the summer, Joe and Kerry had increasingly become "personae non gratae" among a few district managers. Big transitions were on the horizon.

Kerry returned to Bellingham to complete his studies at Western Washington University. He told Joe that he would return frequently during the winter months for cross-country skiing and kayaking adventures together.

"I'll bring the booze," Kerry promised.

"I'll take you up on that, herring," Joe replied. "We should kayak Lake Wenatchee and the Wenatchee River down to Plain."

"It's a deal, herring," replied Kerry.

CHAPTER SEVENTEEN

Attention to Details

In late September, circumstances evolved rapidly for Joe and Rachael. A letter from his Seattle landlord, Gene Owens, informed Joe that the Mushroom Haus had been sold and that he would have thirty days to vacate the premises.

Suddenly, Joe and Rachael were scrambling for a place to live. Pursuing the most likely option, Joe appealed to Faith Hillman, the business management assistant for the Lake Wenatchee Ranger District, in an effort to secure housing on the compound.

"Faith, our rental has been sold and we're going to have to move out in thirty days. Is there any chance of securing housing on the Lake Wenatchee compound?"

"As a matter of fact, Joe, we have a new vacancy on the compound," she informed him. "Rick Bundy, our lead fire prevention specialist, has been hired for a permanent position in the Siuslaw National Forest. Rick and his wife, Ann, are moving to Oregon. It's a small cabin, but you're welcome to rent the place. It has a great view of Lake Wenatchee from the front picture window."

"That's wonderful news, Faith," said Joe, relieved. "We're used to small cabins. You're a lifesaver."

Hastily moving their belongings from the Mushroom Haus to the new dwelling, Joe and Rachael soon entertained their first visitor to their new home, Raoul Stanford.

"Hi, Raoul," said Joe. "How do you like our new digs?"

"Very nice," he responded. "My wife and I used to live in this cabin, too. Always loved the view of Lake Wenatchee. I'm glad you're both here. We have a new assignment for you and Rachael."

Raoul explained, "The Regional Office is forming a team of fire prevention specialists to help patrol a particularly fire-prone area north of Pasadena on the Angeles National Forest. You two have been selected to represent the Wenatchee National Forest on this detail."

In Forest Service parlance, a "detail" involves the temporary transfer of an employee to another position off-district. Details are typically short-term assignments.

"They've asked all the forests in the region to send two district employees with tanker trucks to report to the Los Angeles River Ranger District immediately for the assignment," Raoul continued. "What do you think?"

"It sounds like an adventure," replied Joe. "When do we leave?"

"Immediately," said Raoul. "When you get settled here, check in with Eugene up in the office. He has a lead for a potential wintertime assignment for you to consider."

Joe was elated by the prospect of a road trip. In this case, it would be all-expenses-paid. In his incessant search for adventure, he longed to travel, and Rachael was agreeable after a summer in a remote guard station. Often dreaming of seeing the country, Joe needed new experiences to broaden his perspective on the world.

He was also intrigued by the possibility of a wintertime assignment. Working as a seasonal employee had its advantages—free time and the opportunity to travel. But economically, his savings would typically diminish before his new seasonal appointment could begin. Eugene explained that he had received a call from Steve Devaney, the recreation staff officer on the Mt. Baker-Snoqualmie National Forest.

"Steve says he needs an editor for the environmental impact statement on the Alpine Lakes Planning Team in Seattle," said Eugene. "Apparently, he learned about your freelance work for *The Oregonian* and the *Wenatchee World*. I told him you had a journalism degree and that you wrote the wilderness action plans for the district. I said you would be perfect for the assignment. Steve said he could extend your appointment for another six months to work on the team if you're interested."

"Heck, yes," Joe replied enthusiastically.

"Great, as soon as you return from this fire prevention detail in Southern California, you can begin," said Eugene. "You'll need to commute to Seattle weekly."

"No problem," said Joe. "What a great opportunity."

"I'll call Steve and confirm your interest," said Eugene.

Hurriedly completing their move into their new cabin on the compound, Joe and Rachael packed whatever they would need for the detail in Los Angeles into her Forest Service truck and left late in the day.

Making it as far as Eugene, they stayed with friends and left early the next morning for the first leg of the trip into California. After driving six hundred miles, Joe and Rachael were beat. Moving from the Mushroom Haus into a new home had taken its toll, so they stopped for the night at a Best Western adjacent to the American River in downtown Sacramento.

The next morning, they pushed through the long stretch of Interstate 5 in the San Joaquin Valley, only stopping in Buttonwillow for lunch and a full tank of gas. Maneuvering through the Grapevine toward Los Angeles, they veered left on Interstate 210 toward Pasadena. Arriving at the Los Angeles River Ranger Station at about four p.m., they were greeted by the district's fire management officer (FMO) Dale Moses.

"We thought you two got lost or something," he said when they arrived.

"We had a late start because we had just moved," explained Joe. "But we're here now."

Moses gave Joe and Rachael a brief overview of their assignment. Along with the other personnel sent from the Pacific Northwest, they would staff checkpoints and patrol the canyons north of Pasadena—Big Tujunga, Little Tujunga, Pacoima, and Soledad.

"All cars passing the checkpoints will have their license plates recorded," Moses explained.

"What's been the problem?" asked Joe.

"We've had a number of brush fires started over the past month and we suspect arson," replied Moses. "Considering how dry it's been, along with the intense Santa Ana winds, a fire of epic proportions is expected unless we catch the perpetrators."

Moses then provided directions to the hotel where Joe and Rachael would be staying—the Granada Inn Motel on Sepulveda Boulevard in San Fernando, a short drive from Pasadena.

"You'll meet the rest of the team from Region Six at the hotel," Moses concluded. "The region has sent two prevention guards each from the Mt. Baker-Snoqualmie, Okanagan, Gifford-Pinchot, Mt. Hood, Willamette, Deschutes, Fremont, Siskiyou, and of course, you two from the Wenatchee National Forest."

When Joe and Rachael arrived at the motel, they met some of the other seasonal employees from Washington and Oregon. They soon learned that the fire season had been intense in the Angeles National Forest.

The Forest Service wasn't going to take chances on a big blowup that could threaten lives, homes, and personal property adjacent to federal land. Apparently, many "recreationists" venture into the hills north of Pasadena to shoot firearms. Some start brush fires to flush out rabbits and other small game in the tall grasses prevalent in the area.

"The women will staff the checkpoints and the men will patrol the territory within the checkpoints," said Bob Morrison, one of the Region Six prevention guards, at the team's breakfast the next morning. "The goal is to catch potential arsonists before they leave the vicinity."

"Makes sense," responded Joe. "Nice accommodations here, considering we're seasonal employees."

"Yes, they take care of us," Bob replied. "This place has a swimming pool, too. We have to work every day we're here, but it will pay off in the long run. In addition to our salary, we'll receive overtime and per diem. By the way, a few of us might rent a car after work sometime and take a cruise to Laguna Beach. You interested?"

"Sure," said Joe. "A trip to the beach would be nice."

Rachael and Joe's room on the second floor of the Granada Inn included a balcony that overlooked a courtyard and the swimming pool. The suite featured two queen beds and a sitting room with a television.

"Beats the hell out that Best Western in Sacramento, doesn't it?" asked Joe.

"It sure does," said Rachael.

"Our first order of business is to eat and then find a liquor store in the neighborhood," said Joe.

For the next two months, their routine would include breakfast at the hotel restaurant, where the cooks would also prepare sack lunches for each member of the team. Reporting to the Los Angeles River Ranger Station, the group then received their daily assignments. Moses juggled the various locations among team members for variety.

The Angeles National Forest provided a stark contrast to the forests of the Pacific Northwest. The terrain featured primarily hilly grasslands, with an occasional patch of oak trees at the bottoms of drainages where water flowed. One time, while stopping near the pass to Soledad Canyon for a break, Joe jumped when a rattlesnake lurched his way. Alarmed, he grabbed his shovel and severed the snake's head with the recently sharpened tool.

Day after day, week after week through October and into November, the crew staffed checkpoints and patrolled the canyons north of Pasadena. The air temperature in the Los Angeles Basin remained a consistent ninety-degrees Fahrenheit during the daytime, and the Santa Ana winds gusted relentlessly. Santa Anas are strong, extremely dry downslope winds that originate inland and affect the entire Los Angeles area.

Originating from high-pressure air masses, Santa Ana winds are known for the hot, dry climate they bring in autumn—often the hottest time of the year. To make matters worse, Santa Anas—known as "devil winds"—feature low relative humidity. Together with high temperatures, Santa Anas are infamous for fanning wildfires.

One day after work, Rachael and Joe took up Bob Morrison's offer to take a cruise down the Pacific Coast Highway. They saw many of the Los Angeles beaches made famous by the Beach Boys, including Hermosa Beach. Arriving at Laguna Beach, Joe tried his hand at body surfing, but on his first attempt, he was viciously body-slammed into the sand.

"I had no idea that sand could be so hard," he told Rachael, looking for a bit of sympathy. "I won't be doing that again."

By late November, the detail was starting to take its toll on the team from the Pacific Northwest. Some crew members grew increasingly anxious because the two-month mark had passed. In their daily staff meeting, one crew member asked Moses, "When do you think we're going to be able to go home? We must prepare for winter before the snows fly."

Dale Moses's answer was succinct: "Just as soon as it rains."

A few days later, Sally Bauer, a prevention guard from the Gifford Pinchot National Forest, asked Rachael and Joe if they were interested in visiting Disneyland.

"We'll have to leave right after we get off work to have enough time to enjoy Disneyland before it closes," Sally added.

"Heck, yeah," said Joe. "Anything to break the monotony of our daily routine. Will you be driving?"

"No," she replied. "I thought you would."

"I only have our Forest Service tanker truck," responded Joe. "If we're bold enough to take it to Disneyland, we'll have to keep it quiet because we won't be on official business."

"That's fine with me," said Sally.

After work the next day, Joe, Rachael, and Sally maneuvered through Los Angeles traffic to Anaheim. The trio took advantage of the small crowd at Disneyland that day and enjoyed the big attractions, especially Pirates of the Caribbean. They wrapped things up with a meal at the Blue Bayou Café before driving back to San Fernando. The following day, the crew was notified that they would be moving to a different hotel in Arcadia, closer to their patrol areas.

A week before Thanksgiving, a fire broke out in Big Tujunga Canyon. One of the prevention guards logged a license plate number that led to the apprehension and arrest of a suspected arsonist who had set a brush fire. The crew celebrated their success that evening in the hotel bar. The next day, a Pacific front brought rain, and the crew was released to return home.

"Job well done, folks," announced Moses as he said farewell to the fire prevention technicians from the Pacific Northwest.

Driving back to Lake Wenatchee, Joe and Rachael took brief pit stops in Eugene and Portland before arriving at their new cabin. It hadn't snowed yet, but there was much to do—mainly cutting and stacking as much firewood as possible before celebrating Thanksgiving.

Meanwhile, Kerry—who had completed his degree requirements in environmental engineering—moved to Seattle and was dating Kimberly Shilts, a gorgeous redhead who worked as a landscape architect and owned a small bungalow near the University of Washington campus. Kerry moved in with Kimberly and started applying for jobs. Hired at Olympus Environmental, Kerry was now gainfully employed in his field of work.

After Thanksgiving, Joe began his new position as a writer/editor for the Alpine Lakes Planning Team in downtown Seattle.

The Alpine Lakes detail was expected to last six months, so Joe arranged for accommodations in Seattle during the week. Fortunately, he had friends from his Forest Service days in Prairie City now living in Burien—Garth and Haley Soderling—who offered Joe temporary quarters through January before they would move to Maple Valley.

On his first day on the job, Joe met the team leader, Frank Mathews, research forester. The other principals included Steve Devaney, recreation assistant; Jim Hemming, forestry assistant; Gordon Sites, cartography assistant; Keith Sammons, landscape architect; and Dan Beatty, transportation planner. In addition to the principals, two forestry technicians from each district on the Mt. Baker-Snoqualmie National Forest and the Wenatchee National Forest were selected for the unique detail. Collectively, they would contribute to the first drafts of the plan.

In addition to Joe, the forestry technicians included seasonal employees Maria Finnes from Leavenworth, Steve Fenter and Ellen Zimmerman from Skykomish, Maureen Reilly and Steve Burbach from North Bend, and Pat Hartford and Valerie Hoyer from Ellensburg/Cle Elum. Other ancillary team members included hydrologists, geologists, soil scientists, historical preservationists, and other specialists who would contribute to the document.

After introductions, Frank provided Joe with an overview of his roles and responsibilities. As Frank showed Joe his cubicle, he could hardly believe his eyes. Located next to a window on the twelfth floor of a high-rise in downtown Seattle, Joe could see Pike Place Market directly below his desk. His view also included Elliott Bay and the stunning Olympic Mountains to the west.

"Steve Devaney tells me you have experience in writing and editing," said Frank.

"Yes, I graduated in journalism from the University of Oregon, and I've worked as a writer and editor for a number of newspapers," replied Joe.

"And you currently work as a wilderness ranger for the Lake Wenatchee Ranger District," continued Frank. "Are you familiar with the Alpine Lakes Wilderness Area?"

"Yes, I've patrolled much of that area north of Icicle Creek," Joe responded.

"Perfect," said Frank. "We can really use you. Right now, we have the first draft of an eight-hundred-page environmental impact statement that will require regular editing and revision over the next six months. We have numerous writers contributing to the document, so we will need you as editor to make it sound like it was written by one person. Are you up for that?"

Mt. Hinman from Cathedral Pass in the Alpine Lakes Wilderness

"Absolutely," said Joe.

"The hours will be long," warned Frank. "We'll work twelve hours a day, five days a week."

"Yes, I'm up for the task," replied Joe.

"Great, you can begin right away," Frank replied.

This will be a sweet gig, Joe thought. *Lots of overtime pay and a great workspace with an outstanding view.*

Joe's week consisted of rising early on Mondays at Lake Wenatchee, and driving two-to-three hours into downtown Seattle to begin work at six a.m. After working twelve-hour days, Joe would walk down the long flights of stairs from the Pike Place Market to his Toyota Hilux pickup truck, have a couple of rum and Cokes at the Starlight Lounge, and then drive home to Burien.

Garth and Haley's home was located across the street from the airport. Though they had become accustomed to airplane traffic, Joe would take a while to acclimate to the constant noise. But Joe's time in Burien would be brief. The Alpine Lakes Planning Team broke for the holidays from Christmas through New Year's Day, and the Soderlings moved to Maple Valley, so Joe would need to make new living arrangements.

Back home at Lake Wenatchee for the holidays, Joe resumed cutting firewood and playing on a city league basketball team. The team consisted of Forest Service seasonal employees who were laid off for the winter, and they competed well with teams from Cashmere, Wenatchee, and East Wenatchee.

In the second game on the schedule, Joe went down with a bad ankle sprain. The injury was severe enough that Brian Townsend, Carli's husband and coach of the team, rushed Joe to Cascade General Hospital.

After reviewing x-rays of the injury, the emergency room physician said, "Joe, the bone's not broken, but you have serious ligament damage. We'll wrap you up and you'll be on crutches for a few weeks. I'm afraid you're done for the season as far as basketball is concerned."

"Thanks, doc," responded Joe.

Back at home, Rachael tended to Joe, and he lay flat on his back in bed. The next morning, he awoke with searing pain emanating up and down his leg. Begging Rachael for help, she quickly removed the bandage. Joe's left leg was completely black and blue from his knee to his toes.

"Thanks, Rachael," acknowledged Joe. "The bandage was wrapped way too tightly."

In retrospect, the doctor had applied the bandage before the swelling process was complete. Rachel rewrapped the bandage and Joe immediately felt better, though he remained flat on his back for several days before he attempted to walk with crutches.

Great, thought Joe, *next week I'm going to have to negotiate hundreds of stairs from my parking spot on the waterfront through the Pike Place Market to the office on crutches.*

His working life would indeed become more of a challenge. Now, without a place to crash, Joe had to live out of his truck. The pickup had an enclosed canopy that would serve as his sleeping area for the next few months. He became an urban transient living on the streets of Seattle.

On most days, he bunked in the back of his truck in the parking area below the Alaskan Way viaduct along the western waterfront facing Elliott Bay. The location provided the easiest access to his office. Considering his work schedule, his existence became a routine of work and sleep.

Occasionally, just to escape the sketchy waterfront neighborhood, he would park overnight in the Washington Arboretum managed by the University of Washington Botanic Gardens.

His assignment continued into April. Driving over Stevens Pass weekly could have been more of an issue during most years. But this winter, the weather cooperated—it snowed only a few times. The exception came one Monday morning on his way to Seattle in a blizzard when he witnessed an eighteen-wheeler slide off the highway and tumble into the Nason Creek Valley below, horrifying eyewitnesses.

Joe continued to struggle on crutches to negotiate the stairs from the waterfront through the end of his time on the Alpine Lakes Planning Team. One morning before dawn, as Joe slowly inched his way up the stairs, he came face-to-snout with what looked like a rat the size of a dog. Seeing Joe in the dim lighting, the rat bared its teeth and snarled as if to attack. Joe cautiously gave the creature a wide berth as he maneuvered with his crutches up the stairs.

"You won't believe what I saw on the stairs through the market this morning," Joe announced when he arrived in the office. "I think it was a giant rat!"

"You must have seen a wharf rat," explained Frank. "Nasty critters. They hang out down on the waterfront. They're from a superfamily of rats known as Muroidea. They can grow to be well over a foot long. Wharf rats hop off ships that dock in the port and look for food along the waterfront."

"Scared the shit out of me," said Joe. "I wasn't going to mess with it."

"Good thinking," said Frank.

In February, the 1980 Winter Olympics began in Lake Placid, New York. Frank, a former youth hockey player from Vancouver, British Columbia, was closely monitoring the exploits of the US hockey team. He brought a television to work so that everyone in the office could watch a group of American college kids challenge professionals from the best hockey teams in the world—the Soviet Union, Finland, and Sweden.

As the team worked in a frenzied effort to meet the April 1 deadline, they also witnessed perhaps the most dramatic upsets in Olympic history. The underdog US hockey team defeated the defending gold-medal-winning Soviet team before an enthusiastic home crowd in Lake Placid, New York. Two days later, the Americans defeated Finland 4–2 to clinch the gold medal. The victories would come to be called the "Miracle on Ice."

At the end of March, Joe was assigned to drive copies of the plan's final draft to ranger district offices in Skykomish, Lake Wenatchee, Leavenworth, Ellensburg, Cle Elum, and North Bend, completing the circuit in a day. Once the districts approved the plan, Joe and the other forestry technicians were laid off. Joe returned to Lake Wenatchee to await his next assignment after the required sixty-day break.

That spring, Joe's grandmother passed away. Iva Maria Sanguineti had raised Joe while his father, an itinerant high school instructor, pursued teaching jobs in various small towns in Oregon. Iva was his guiding light throughout his young life, and she taught Joe to be loyal, helpful, and kind. Yet despite his upbringing, Joe could be edgy and irascible at times. Perhaps because of his Italian heritage, he could be also menacing when provoked.

“I’m Italian,” he liked to tell Kerry. “We don’t call the cops; we call family.”

After attending the memorial service for his *nonna* in Portland with the rest of his family, Joe returned to Lake Wenatchee. Inconsolable for several weeks, Joe fell into a deep funk.

CHAPTER EIGHTEEN

Range of Darkness

Initially, Kerry enjoyed his new job. Olympus Environmental provided engineering expertise to a variety of clients on the design of earthwork, stormwater, waste treatment, waste repository, streams and wetlands restoration, dredging, and other projects. Kerry, trained to manage environmental remediation efforts, would help assure compliance with various regulations related to pollution prevention, permitting, and auditing.

Yet after just six months, Kerry grew increasingly antsy. He continued to suffer from mental anguish caused by bouts of episodic depression. He enjoyed his work at Olympus but felt his team wasn't driven to excel to the same degree that he was. He suddenly felt compelled to make a change. Learning that Olympus Environmental had a satellite office in Helena, Kerry applied for a transfer to the company's Montana office.

He explained his dilemma to Kimberly, and she was empathetic. Kimberly had lived in Washington for many years and liked the notion of living in Big Sky Country. She told Kerry she was "all in" on the prospect. When management approved his transfer, Kerry and Kimberly started actively planning the move.

First, Kerry drove to Helena and purchased a house. Meanwhile, Kimberly listed her house for sale and prepared to move to Montana. Kerry then called Joe and left a message at the Lake Wenatchee Ranger Station to call him as soon as possible. When the two connected, Kerry informed Joe of his move to Montana.

"I have a good-paying job here in Seattle," he told Joe. "But meaning and purpose are what I really want when it comes to my career. I don't feel like I have that in Seattle. The opportunity for a change in venue for the same company was compelling."

"But I thought Seattle was your ideal," Joe responded.

"It has been," Kerry replied. "But I need more than just a city. I need to feel like I'm accomplishing something significant in my life's work."

"Let me know if you need any help moving, mein herring," added Joe.

"I will," said Kerry.

Almost immediately, Kerry inexplicably had cold feet and experienced serious doubts about the move to Montana. He agonized over whether he had made the right choice in pulling up stakes. Soon, he had made his decision. Kerry called Kimberly and told her that she shouldn't sell her home in Seattle and that he was coming home.

Kerry then called a friend to help him move back. When he arrived in Seattle, Kimberly was obliged to have a "come to Jesus" meeting with Kerry.

"Kerry, I can't continue to live with you this way," Kimberly announced. "You're driven to work and driven to live, but you're reckless. You're driving yourself off a cliff, and I can't seem to be able to help you. You have no loyalty to any employer, and you apparently have no loyalty to me."

"I'm sorry, Kerry," she concluded. "I've enjoyed our time and our adventures together, but I need something more than you can provide. This is good-bye."

Heartbroken, Kerry moved out of Kimberly's house and stayed with friends. He remained in a deep depression for several weeks. Having fallen into the depths of the abyss, he lost touch with friends and family. Almost a year after their last discussion, Kerry learned that Joe's beloved grandmother had passed away, so he composed a letter.

Mein herring:

I'm very sorry to hear of the loss of your beloved grandmother. I understand you're feeling a wide range of emotions, and I can relate to how you're dealing with your loss. My situation is not good here. In just two months, I've lost my job, my house, and my girlfriend. I think I'm losing my mind.

Ever since I broke up with Kimberly after my aborted attempt to move to Montana, I have been in a constant state of depression. I recently had my thyroid checked to see why I'm so chilled all the time. Apparently, a whacked thyroid can contribute to depression. The results came back well within the norm, which disappoints me because I'm looking for clues.

Each day gets increasingly worse, and now it seems unbearable. Some friends took me to a psychiatrist the other day. Right now, I am staying with various friends, couch-surfing and relying on them for dinners and company. They all have been very empathetic and loving. I can't seem to sleep. I try reading while waiting for the sleep medication to take effect. Morning comes way too soon.

I have been attempting to stay busy, but there is little or nothing to do. Each day is very long, and I really stress out over that. I have been working with a counselor for months and have tried five or six antidepressants. But my condition only seems to get worse all the time. I have made bad decisions that are making me less independent. Things are severe, mein herring.

To be completely truthful and honest with you, I have been plagued by depression all my life, even when we lived in the Mushroom Haus. However, with my most recent ill-fated move, I feel crushed alive. My life seems to be turning to shit.

I can only say that I have always cherished our friendship and admired your spirit. You are a true friend and an inspiration to me. God bless you. Eight months is a long time for the worst I have ever felt in my life.

Here is my final thought. Together, we are experiencing the whole range of darkness. We have both been through periods of depression before and have come out the other end richer and with a deeper appreciation for all things. As the demons plague you with grief and doubts, remember that you are the same person you've always been and will always be.

Everything changes and nothing changes. You will come out the other side intact. You are the best you have ever been as well as the least. The best wins, always.

You will make it through this period of sadness and become your whole self again. That much is certain. We have both experienced it. You are the exact same Joe Blanco who has stood on top of Cascade peaks. You always will be.

Much love to you and Rachael, who is also an incredible inspiration to me.

Love, Kerry

CHAPTER NINETEEN

Barbarians at the Gate

In April, while awaiting news about their summer assignments, it was becoming clear to Joe that his prospects of being rehired at the Lake Wenatchee Ranger District were increasingly dismal. The Mushroom Haus had achieved a level of notoriety that had raised some eyebrows in the district, affecting his reputation among two new managers with influence on hiring decisions.

Then, the new fire management officer (FMO), Bane Keller, learned that Joe and Rachael had taken a Forest Service vehicle to Disneyland, a clear rule violation of using federal vehicles "for official use only." Consequently, Keller directed the district's business management assistant to pass on Joe Blanco, Kerry Weiss, and Rachael White when hiring seasonals for the coming summer.

Jan Oliver, the timber management assistant, had told Carli Townsend, "Joe Blanco and Kerry Weiss are bad influences on the other seasonal employees in the district."

"Oh, but I really like those two characters," Carli responded in their defense.

"Those two characters, as you call them, are hooligans," added Bane Keller. "They have no respect for authority and are clearly a flashpoint for trouble."

"But they're very popular with all the seasonal employees," replied Carli.

"Exactly, but the two of them are bad influences" came Keller's response. “That’s why we need to make sure they’re not rehired in this district.”

Rachael and Joe were subsequently passed over for hire on the Lake Wenatchee Ranger District and were picked up by the Entiat Ranger District instead.

“I can’t believe we weren’t rehired at Lake Wenatchee,” said an incredulous Rachael, unaware of the nefarious subterfuge occurring behind the scenes.

“I have a pretty good idea why,” said Joe, who was hardwired with the district grapevine through Carli. “Those people are easy to read. Keller and Oliver were able to exert their influence to assure that we wouldn’t cause any trouble around here anymore.”

Rachael would be rehired on the tree planting crew at Lake Wenatchee, a short-term job, but the two were required to vacate their cabin on the compound to make way for new summer hires. With no place to go, Joe and Rachael were invited to stay at Flynn and Lydia Stein’s home in Chiwawa River Pines until they would need to move to Entiat.

“I can’t tell you how much I appreciate your offer,” Joe told Flynn. “You and Lydia are life-savers.”

As Rachael worked on the tree planting crew at Lake Wenatchee, Joe spent his days looking for suitable quarters in Entiat, a small town on the Columbia River just north of Wenatchee.

The village resides on what residents charmingly call Lake Entiat, which is basically the Columbia River backwater behind Rocky Reach Dam. In the 1950s, Entiat had been flooded by the creation of the dam, and most of the town’s buildings and facilities were relocated to higher ground. Before they began construction on Rocky Reach Dam, the Chelan County Public Utility District had claimed eminent domain with some local property owners, then worked with developers to plan a new town site.

For Joe and Rachael, Entiat would be a radical transition from Lake Wenatchee. But a job was a job, so they accepted their positions in the Entiat Ranger District. The Entiat River Valley divides the Entiat Mountains from the Chelan Mountains. Due to massive project fires that burned hundreds of thousands of acres in the Entiat Valley in the early 1970s, the landscape is dominated by wildfire ecology.

As Joe searched for a place to live, pickings were slim for rentals. Then, he stumbled onto low-income apartments with a view overlooking Lake Entiat. The facility was new, and the rent was reasonable, just $150 a month. What's more, Joe had the first choice among the twenty or so apartments available, so he chose the one with the best view.

Returning to the Steins' household at Chiwawa River Pines after signing the lease, Joe announced that he had found a place to live.

"The apartment is so new you can smell the formaldehyde," said Joe with a laugh. "But Entiat itself is kind of a Podunk town with little to offer in the way of amenities."

"Entiat may not be as bad as you think, Joe," Flynn said reassuringly. "Yes, it's a different environment than Lake Wenatchee, but Entiat has its own unique features and charms."

"You mean like cowboys and rednecks?" Joe asked sarcastically.

"Well, yes, there's that," said Flynn. "But it's much dryer and warmer down there. You might be surprised. It might grow on you, as it did with me. Remember, I was on the Entiat Bushmen Interagency Hotshot Crew."

"Yes, I remember, Flynn," said Joe. "I've been on project fires with those dudes. They're a bunch of hand puppets with bad attitudes. I don't know how you survived the experience."

"It was my first job out of college," said Flynn, who had graduated from the University of Wisconsin-Lacrosse in recreation and parks management.

"I applied for Forest Service jobs in Washington and a position with the Bushmen was the job I was offered," Flynn said. "After one season, Lake Wenatchee offered me the position of recreation crew foreman."

"At least you won't have to work with the Bushmen," Flynn added with a laugh.

In May, Joe and Rachael moved to their new apartment, which was within walking distance from the Entiat District Ranger Station. Settled into their new apartment at Entiat Gardens, Joe and Rachael started work on Monday, May 12.

Joe had been hired as the Blue Creek backcountry ranger, and Rachael would work on a two-person timber stand analysis crew. Joe's assignment was to patrol the Mad River area in the Entiat Mountains by motorcycle. Blue Creek, where he would be stationed, was nearly fifty miles from Entiat but conveniently located only ten miles from Lake Wenatchee using Forest Service roads.

Rachael would work on a two-person crew with Kevin Bannon, the foreman, conducting fuels analysis in old fire sites and timber sales. Kevin, a native of nearby Quincy, was a forestry major at Washington State University. A former Bushman, he had the same macho, chauvinist attitude as the rest of the crew of Neanderthals on the Entiat Interagency Hotshot Crew, as Rachael would soon come to learn.

Meanwhile, Joe began his first week as the Blue Creek backcountry guard. He would be required to ride a Honda motorcycle to the trailhead of the upper Mad River trail. The trek by motorbike was long, starting up the Entiat River Road about nine miles to Ardenvoir, an unincorporated village with a post office and little else.

Initially, Ardenvoir was a logging/mining camp built by the Civilian Conservation Corps in the 1930s, but later the Forest Service built a work center. In addition to serving as a staging area for projects, the work center provided housing for several Forest Service employees.

From Ardenvoir, Joe turned left on the Tillicum Creek Road, climbing a long hill to Mosquito Ridge on the crest of Entiat Ridge. Once on the ridge, he followed the ridgetop road as it passed Sugarloaf Lookout to Maverick Saddle, followed by five miles of trail to the guard station. The trip to Blue Creek was about eighty miles roundtrip and took about four hours on semi-improved logging roads and trails.

Well, at least I get paid for a lot of travel time, Joe thought.

On the following Saturday, their day off, Joe took Rachael up to see the Blue Creek Guard Station tucked away in the upper Mad River area. They drove their truck to the trailhead at Maverick Saddle and hiked the five miles into Blue Creek for the night.

"You're going to have to stay here?" Rachael asked. "It's not exactly airtight. Won't it have rats and bugs?"

"Yeah, that's what they tell me," Joe replied. "At least it has a roof to keep me dry in a rainstorm. I can deal with vermin and insects. Beats staying here in a tent."

The next morning, Joe and Rachael hiked back to Maverick Saddle. Approaching the trailhead, they saw clouds quickly rolling in.

"Let's skedaddle before it starts raining," suggested Joe.

Suddenly, instead of rain, it started to snow. At least it looked like snow.

"What's this?' asked Rachael. "Snow?"

"Impossible," Joe replied. "It can't be snow. It's about sixty degrees Fahrenheit right now."

"It looks like snow, but it seems to be gritty," noted Rachael after collecting a sample.

"Yes, and it smells strange," said Joe. "Weird! Let's get a move-on."

What they didn't know then—but would soon find out—was that morning, Mount St. Helens in southwestern Washington erupted after an earthquake of 5.0 magnitude. The entire north side of the summit slid down the mountain.

Following a giant landslide of rock and ice, an enormous explosion of steam and volcanic gases surged northward along the ground at high speed. The lateral blast stripped trees from most of its hilly slopes within six miles of the volcano and destroyed vegetation as far as twelve miles away. Approximately ten million trees were flattened by the blast, and the mountain sent a plume of ash in a northeasterly direction with the prevailing winds.

Returning to their apartment, Joe and Rachael learned that a massive cloud of smoke and ash was heading their way. Advised by Wenatchee media to remain indoors and avoid driving because of potential damage to their vehicles, North Central Washington residents hunkered down for the next twenty-four hours.

Grabbing his camera, Joe rushed outside and took pictures of the massive ash cloud moving up the Columbia River toward Entiat.

At the next district meeting, Joe and Ron Paxson, another backcountry ranger in the district, hatched a plan to try to market some of the ash from Mt. St. Helens, which had blanketed all of Eastern Washington.

"I have an idea, Joe," said Paxson. "Let's take a little trip down to Moses Lake and collect some ash. We can package small samples in glass vials and sell them back East. We can advertise the vials in *The New York Times*."

"I like it," replied Joe, who was always a sucker for a get-quick-rich-scheme.

When they arrived in Moses Lake, they saw the ash—stacked in piles on the side of the road like snow—was ready-at-hand everywhere. But what they hadn't anticipated was the sheer density of the ash. They could barely fill the bottom of a garbage sack before the weight of the ash became too much for the plastic. In short, the ash was quite heavy. Consequently, their plan never got off the ground.

Joe sighed. "Another in a long line of failed boondoggles."

By June, with the season in full swing. Joe spent his weeks at the Blue Creek Guard Station. Rachael worked out of the Entiat Ranger Station conducting fuel plot surveys with Kevin Bannon. Otherwise, she kept the home fires burning while Joe patrolled the Mad River Country. Much to his surprise, Joe came to appreciate his new gig, mostly because the Mad River area of the Entiat Mountains is unique and beautiful.

The verdant meadowlands, with colorful names like Whistling Pig, Cougar, and Blue Creek, were unlike anything he had ever seen—all high mountain plateaus with gorgeous ponds, such as

Mad Lake, Two Little Lakes, and Kelly Lake. His patrol area also featured numerous loop trips and viewpoints from Cougar Mountain and Klone Peak, both nearly seven thousand feet.

The structure that functioned as the Blue Creek Guard Station was built during "the great civilizations of antiquity," as Joe liked to say. Little more than an embellished hunter's cabin, the structure had been constructed in the 1920s. The one-room cabin had beds and bedding, along with a makeshift kitchen with cabinets and a picnic table.

Not exactly airtight, as Rachael had surmised, the guard station was consistently infested with rodents and insects of all shapes, sizes, and varieties. Periodically, a lovesick coyote would sneak up on the cabin at night and let out a high-volume yowl, scaring the bejeebers out of Joe. Yet the structure was functional, and it did at least provide shelter from wet weather. He had his AM-FM radio for music.

As for communication with the outside world, Joe had his Forest Service radio. Unfortunately, the Blue Creek Guard Station was so remote that he couldn't communicate directly with the Entiat Ranger Station. He would have to relay his messages to the home office through Laurel Oliver, the Sugarloaf Lookout, using Channel 1.

With no point in monitoring radio traffic on Channel 2, the frequency used by the Entiat and Chelan Ranger districts, Joe kept the dial on Channel 1, where he could track communications on the Lake Wenatchee Ranger District, keeping up with the likes of Fergie, the Dogman, Gottlieb, and his other compadres from the Aldo Leopold Society.

Though she worked diligently, Rachael wasn't enjoying her new position at all. Her supervisor, Kevin Bannon, would berate her performance because she wasn't able to develop the skills necessary for fuel plot analysis as quickly as he liked. As a former Bushman, he simply had no patience with the concept of women doing men's work. When assigned to project fires, Rachael found the harassment from Kevin and his Bushmen brethren unbearable.

Joe knew that the Bushmen considered themselves "fire gods" and that they all had inflated opinions of themselves. But he saw through their charade; he knew that they only were defined by their large egos and small brains and often told Rachael that Bushmen were "all hat and no cowboy."

Eventually, Rachael admitted, "I can't sleep at night. It's become a real problem. Kevin and his buddies continually torment me, and it seems to be getting worse."

"That's all I need to hear," said Joe, incensed. "I'll take care of this myself."

On Monday morning, Joe strolled into the fire management office and approached Ken Lester, the assistant FMO. "Les," as he was called, was a smarmy career fire manager.

"What can I do for you, Blanco?" asked Les, who had his feet propped up on his desk.

"Rachael can't sleep at night because of the ongoing harassment by Kevin Bannon and many of his Bushmen buddies," announced Joe. "It's starting to affect my life and I don't like it."

Les removed his feet from his desk and sat up straight in his chair. "What do you mean?"

"Let me be perfectly clear, Les," Joe continued. "The harassment by Kevin Bannon and his band of cowboys must stop. Otherwise, we'll have to have a little clambake with you, me, Rachael, and the forest supervisor, a personal friend of mine. If not, I'll be more than happy to kick each and every one of their asses."

Contrite, Lester assured Joe that he would "talk to them" about their behavior. At the next district meeting, an otherwise rambunctious crowd of seasonal employees hushed when Joe walked into the room. Knowing the grapevine worked quickly, Joe took their response as a measure of success. After that, Joe became a pariah among the Bushmen and their acolytes.

But Joe's mission had been accomplished. The Bushmen and most of the fire management staff left Rachael alone, and they generally avoided Joe.

In August, Joe received a call from Kerry. "I'm coming over from Seattle with a couple of kayaks to paddle Lake Entiat and the lower Entiat River. You up for some paddling next week, mein herring? I'll bring the mushrooms."

"Well, my good herring, to paraphrase *Alice in Wonderland*, I suppose I ought to eat or drink something or other," replied Joe.

"Excellent," affirmed Kerry. "I'll bring the Dogman and his girlfriend, Conifer A. Coil, Ross Roget, and Paul Kirchmeier with me. We shall have a mushroom party."

On their way to Entiat from Lake Wenatchee, the group stopped at Ross's place, a fruit picker's shack located in a large orchard in Peshastin. When they arrived, Ross learned that his home had been burglarized while he had been gone, so he bailed on the trip to Entiat and called the Chelan County Sheriff's Office to report the crime. Meanwhile, the others continued to Entiat.

Arriving at Entiat Gardens, Kerry asked Joe, "Are we stocked on beverages, mein herring?"

"Nope, I'll need to run up to the market," replied Joe.

Finally settled for the evening, the group consumed mushrooms and watched old Monty Python skits on television. After the mushrooms took effect, they delved into deep discussions about the meaning of life and the philosophies of Plato and Aristotle, Hegel and Kant, Descartes and Rousseau, Epicurus and Socrates, and Confucius and Laozi. Later they discussed their favorite authors of the day, including Ken Kesey, Tom Wolfe, and Hunter S. Thompson.

As the night progressed, the next-door neighbors started arguing at high volume. The walls of the apartment building were paper-thin, so the drug-addled group grew increasingly anxious as the shouting and screaming intensified. The young married couple with a small child next door sounded like they would kill each other at any moment.

"What's with the bickering Bickersons next door?" asked Kerry.

"They have issues," replied Joe, "Let's all take a walk."

"Good idea," agreed Conifer.

They all strolled down to the park on Lake Entiat to watch the sunrise come over the hill above Orondo. Afterward, the Dogman, Conifer, and Paul departed for the return trip to Lake Wenatchee. Kerry and Joe spent the rest of the day kayaking on the Columbia and Entiat Rivers.

Laid off in September, Rachael learned that the old house in Entiat Park was up for rent. After touring the place, Joe and Rachael were sold on the idea of moving out of Entiat Gardens and renting the park house. Though old, the house was large, and their yard was forty acres in size. The rent was only one hundred dollars a month, and it appeared to be an ideal place to spend the winter.

The old structure was quite spacious, about three thousand square feet, and featured four bedrooms, a large kitchen, and a solarium. The front picture window included a stunning view of Lake Entiat and Mission Ridge south of Wenatchee.

"I love it," said Rachael after they moved in. "It sure beats living in that apartment."

"It's perfect," added Joe. "We can live here and collect unemployment for the winter. I'll apply for permanent Forest Service jobs and continue with my freelance writing projects."

At the end of the year, two major news stories occurred that would affect Joe and Rachael deeply. Ronald Reagan was elected president of the United States. Then John Lennon was murdered by Mark David Chapman in New York. Both events cast a pall on the coming holiday season.

CHAPTER TWENTY

Return to the Promised Land

Now settled into a new home in Entiat Park, Joe received a call from Raoul Stanford at the Lake Wenatchee Ranger Station at the end of September.

"Are you laid off now, Joe?" queried Raoul.

"Yes," said Joe. "My season ended here more abruptly than I expected. But I'm not surprised. I won't win any popularity contests in this district."

"You, Joe?" he asked incredulously. "That's impossible."

"It's a long story, Raoul," Joe responded.

"I have good news," Raoul said with his trademark enthusiasm. "I have a couple of month's worth of work for you if you want. We have a cache of funding from the state of Washington to complete an off-road vehicle (ORV) trail in the Chickamin Creek drainage. We'd like to get as much of that trail completed as possible before the snows fly. Otherwise, we'll lose the money. Are you interested?"

"Absolutely, Raoul," replied Joe. "When do we begin?"

"Immediately," said Raoul. "You'll be working with your old friends Ross and Gottlieb on the crew. Plus, you'll be happy to hear I've rehired Kerry Weiss."

"Excellent, Raoul, I'll be there on Monday," acknowledged Joe.

Joe knew what to expect. Few without the experience understand the backbreaking nature of the trail work. On this assignment, the crew would hike several miles every day just to reach the job site, where they would build a new trail. Ross described the project as "the world's longest ditch." It was an apt description.

The crew, already in top shape from a summer of wilderness hiking, found their autumn assignment invigorating. Together again, they had great discussions about art, music, culture, religion, and a veritable potpourri of subjects while they hiked to the job site.

Working as a trail dog once again was both demanding and rewarding. The bonus? Laboring in Valhalla. Watching the needles of western larch turn yellow. Trekking through forests under a warm autumn sun in remote locations that few people get to see.

One day Raoul asked the crew if they were up for a new assignment. "Our aerial observer spotted a squatter's cabin about four miles up the Napeequa River, deep in the Glacier Peak Wilderness. We've been assigned to hike upriver to destroy the cabin and pack out all the garbage."

The US Forest Service policy concerning illicit cabins in the wilderness required that they would be torched, a perfect assignment for former firefighters.

"What do you think, fellows?" asked Raoul.

"Hell, yes" replied Ross. "Anything for a break from the world's longest ditch."

Hiking up the Twin Lakes trail from Napeequa Crossing, the group detoured to the left off the trail and followed the river. Immediately, Raoul bolted ahead, vanishing into the primeval forest. The group had to bushwhack through old-growth cedars eight feet in diameter, Devil's club taller than a house, and prolific vine maple—with no clear route.

As they navigated their way up the canyon, Kerry said to Joe, "I'm expecting a Pteranodon or Pterodactyl to swoop in on us at any moment."

"Where in the hell is Raoul?" Joe asked.

About ten years older than the rest, Raoul nonetheless moved quickly, making the task of maneuvering through the vine maple thickets challenging to keep up with their supervisor.

When the group finally caught up with him, Kerry asked, "What's the rush, Raoul?"

"Sorry, fellas, my toes were cut off in a lawn mower accident as a kid," admitted Raoul. "Now, I'm unable to slow or stop without sitting down."

Raoul then agreed to keep in touch using a verbal signal. Kerry would shout "Raoul!" so the crew could keep track of him as they battled through the thick Cascadian jungle. Raoul would then shout back in response.

Arriving at the squatter's cabin, the group discovered a complex marijuana-growing operation. The elaborate arrangement had a mini-hydropower generation facility complete with paddle wheel, circuits, and outlets providing electricity to the small cabin. After cleaning the abandoned site, Joe placed packets of flammable gel in strategic locations, and Kerry torched the cabin.

The crew stayed long enough to watch most of the dilapidated cabin burn. But when the sun drew low in the sky, they packed the garbage into their backpacks and departed back down the Napeequa River for the return trip to the ranger station.

As September transitioned into October, the crew resumed their work on the "world's longest ditch." At night, Kerry and Joe slept in the back of their pickup trucks near the horse barn. The horses and mules had already been transported to their winter quarters on farms near Yakima, so Joe and Kerry had the facility to themselves. They showered daily at the bunkhouse.

Once again, Carol Winters enlisted Joe as a member of the Plain Players—the little community theater group—to participate in the group's Halloween variety show that would run for three days. Knowing he was a journalist by training, Carol asked Joe to draft and distribute a news release announcing their performances.

With a dateline of Plain, Washington, the news release began:

Just plain folks? Well, not exactly.

The Plain Players, a community theater group based in the

Plain-Lake Wenatchee area, will present a Halloween variety show October 28–30 at the Natapoc Grange, and residents of the upper Wenatchee valley are eagerly anticipating the event.

The show will feature local talent and will include "music, dancing and laughter," according to director Carol Winters. "We're starting a new tradition with this Halloween extravaganza," said Winters, a theater arts graduate from the University of Puget Sound now working as a fire dispatcher for the Lake Wenatchee Ranger District.

"Last Memorial Day weekend, our variety show packed two full houses on consecutive nights with folks coming all the way from Seattle," said Winters. "For our Halloween special, we have a number of 'spook-tacular' surprises in store for the whole family."

Georgia Campbell, emcee of the show, and her husband, Dominic, will perform a singing duet accompanied by Carli Townsend on piano. Loretta and George Harper of Plain will sing an original Halloween ballad, and the Gil Simmons family will perform two musical numbers. The show will also include several comedy sketches featuring Joe Blanco and Kerry Weiss and an original mime act by Gottlieb Hille.

Admission to the show is two dollars for adults and one dollar for children under 12. Proceeds from the show will benefit the Plain-Lake Wenatchee Community Club, which sponsors the Plain Players and other local projects, including Halloween parties and films for children.

The Plain Players, under the direction of Carol Winters and Bryce Newsom, also perform feature-length plays annually. Winters is currently gearing up for a three-act comedy that she hopes to showcase at several locations next summer.

A week after the Halloween special, Raoul informed the crew of stunning news. On a routine late-season patrol, Carol Winters discovered Scott Foresman's bike below the Heather Lake Trailhead. The former Forest Service seasonal employee had been missing and presumed dead for two years.

"For the next week or so, we'll join an interagency search-and-rescue operation to locate his remains in that vicinity," Raoul announced.

"Who found his bike?" asked Kerry.

"Carol Winters was replacing signage in the upper Little Wenatchee River area when she learned that the Heather Lake Trailhead sign was missing," explained Raoul. "She noticed trampled brush nearby, so she followed her senses down the hillside and found the sign and then spotted Scott Foresman's bike."

For the next three days, about thirty Forest Service employees and Chelan County deputies combed the area near the trailhead and up the trail to Heather Lake, trying to locate the missing Foresman. On the third day, Ross Roget had a hunch to head upstream into thick brush at the first creek crossing on the trail. There, he found Scott's remains, along with a rusted pistol.

Along the Heather Lake Trail

"It seemed to be a calculated suicide," observed Ross. "Apparently, he had driven to that spot in the clear-cut where they discovered his car, leading searchers to believe he was climbing Mt. Massif."

"He then rode his bike about thirty-five miles up the Little Wenatchee River to the Heather Lake Trailhead," continued Ross. "He dumped his bike, hiked about a mile up the trail, walked off-trail a short distance, and then shot himself."

"Geez, what an elaborate scheme," observed Joe. "He must have been in a lot of pain."

"He did what he had to do," opined Kerry.

Back on the Chickamin Creek ORV Trail, the crew finished their project in another two weeks. Raoul next had them reassigned to identify and mark spotted owl habitat in the Lake Wenatchee Ranger District.

"Fellas, I have a new assignment for you that we'll focus on for the remainder of the season," Raoul announced. "You'll all be helping Hannah Murray identify and mark sites where we suspect northern spotted owl habitat might be located near planned timber sales on the district."

"Owls?" asked Joe.

"Yes, owls," Raoul replied. "Since spotted owls are nocturnal creatures, you'll need to drive to proposed timber sales and sit quietly while 'hooting' to locate likely candidates.

"Hannah has mapped out several timber sales that will need to be observed for signs of northern spotted owls," continued Raoul. "You'll start right before dark. Drive to your assigned sites and stake out a plot, then start hooting periodically and listen for a response. Your shifts will end at dawn."

"Here's a job we can list on our resumés, mein herring," Kerry said with a grin.

Once the crew was trained to "hoot," they drove to suspected sites near timber sales. Some of the hooters became skilled at matching the call or "hoot" of the northern spotted owl. Others used tape recorders to do their calling for them.

Describing how to establish a position in a suspected site, Hannah instructed the team to sit higher on a slope above where an owl might be nesting because sound travels uphill, not downhill. When a nest was located, the site was marked. Ground crews would then come out during daylight hours to locate and document the nesting sites. The team came to be known as "Hannah's Hooters."

The Endangered Species Act had become the focus of a series of contentious public, political, and legal controversies surrounding the protection of the northern spotted owl (*Strix occidentalis caurina*) on national forest lands in Washington and Oregon.

A medium-sized, dark brown owl with a barred tail, white spots, and dark brown eyes, the northern spotted owl had been designated an "indicator species," meaning an organism whose absence, presence, or abundance reflects a specific environmental condition. Indicator species can signal a change in the biological condition or health of a particular ecosystem.

Northern spotted owls exclusively inhabit old-growth forests, which have the appropriate characteristics required for their nesting, roosting, and foraging. The owls require a multilayered, multispecies canopy with large old-growth timber. The owl had been listed as endangered due to the loss of suitable habitat caused by extensive timber harvesting.

Previously, the Forest Service followed the Northwest Forest Plan, which allowed loggers and timber company executives to work with few or no restrictions. Now, however, wildlife habitat had become an integral part of the "multiple-use" mantra of the Forest Service and the listing of the owl as an endangered species became a hot-button issue among loggers who were used to having free rein.

The debate played out in the national news media and led to hostilities in many of the Pacific Northwest's small towns. Though the issues involved were far more complex than the media portrayed, many reports pitched the controversy as a struggle between loggers and owls, with the Forest Service caught in the middle.

The job lasted six weeks before new snowfall ended the season. With their appointments concluded, Joe and Kerry had decisions to make.

Joe returned to graduate school in journalism at the University of Oregon in Eugene, where Rachael would join him. In December, Joe and Rachael eloped to Las Vegas, married in the famous "Elvis Chapel," and honeymooned in Ensenada, Mexico. Rachael had been "with child" for several months and it was time to "tie the knot."

Kerry found a position in Seattle working for Jacobs Engineering, where his assignments focused on conducting environmental mediation. Kerry decided he would maintain his kayak business as a side gig. Occasionally, he would attend outdoor shows throughout the Northwest to market his kayaks.

Meanwhile, during a kayak expedition in the San Juan Islands, Kerry met Ashleigh Phillips, a journalist and law student at the University of California at Berkeley, and the two soon fell in love.

Ashleigh stayed with Kerry at a house he purchased in the Maple Leaf neighborhood while in Seattle, and commuted to Berkeley to continue her second year of law school. Kerry believed his new-found love interest would change his life for the better.

Kerry was anxious to break the news to Joe, so he gave him a call.

"Mr. Vallindaklopf, so good to hear from you," said Joe. "I have news. Rachael and I have married. We eloped to Las Vegas and honeymooned in Mexico. Now, I'm back in graduate school pursuing a master's degree in public relations."

"That's great news, Doctor Gonzo," said Kerry. "You've made an excellent choice."

"Thanks, herring, but there's more," added Joe. "We're expecting a child."

"Mein herring, I'm very happy for both you and Rachael," Kerry said. "I also have big news. I've met the girl of my dreams. Her name is Ashleigh Phillips and she's not only a sea-kayaking nut and mountain maven like me, but she's a second-year law student at Cal-Berkeley."

"Tell me more, mein freund," Joe prodded.

"Well, she's both brainy and gorgeous, of course," Kerry replied. "She graduated from Cornell before moving West."

"That's excellent, my friend," said Joe. "You've done well for yourself. We must have a summit meeting in the near future to celebrate our mutual good fortune."

"Absolutely," confirmed Kerry. "Let us noodle on a date and then confirm."

Lake Wenatchee and Dirty Face Peak

CHAPTER TWENTY-ONE

Encore in Valhalla

Back in Eugene after his extended hiatus in the wilderness, Joe continued his postgraduate education in journalism, this time with a focus on public relations. He had worked as a reporter and editor, but now with a family to support, Joe needed a more secure financial situation, including health benefits. The field of public relations seemed to offer the security he needed.

While Joe had fully embraced the wonders of nature found in the wilderness, he had not totally rejected urban life. He wanted the best of both worlds. His goal was to be a professional writer living among other people, but with a need to periodically retreat to the solitude of the wilderness to clear his mind and renew his spirit.

For now, his immediate concern was to acquire the appropriate knowledge and credentials to qualify for a position as a public information officer for the USFS, preferably the Wenatchee National Forest. Joe now had family and he knew it wouldn't be easy returning to school with no steady income during the winter months.

His graduate program focused on broadening his skill sets beyond newspaper reporting and management, and to diversify his training regimen, Joe pursued classes in advertising, magazine journalism, and public relations.

In his interdisciplinary track, Joe took classes in art photography, botany, geology, marketing, and any coursework that might make him a more attractive candidate as a public information officer for the Forest Service. Compared to his undergraduate years, Joe was much more focused. He had become a serious student, and anything less than an "A" was unacceptable.

After completing the first year of his graduate program in June 1982, Joe and Rachael relocated to Lake Wenatchee so that he could pull another stint as seasonal Forest Service employee to afford tuition and fees for the final year of graduate school. This time, however, Joe and Rachel had a baby girl in tow. They named her Zoey.

With a family, Joe qualified for better housing on the Lake Wenatchee compound. Faith Hillman offered Joe and Rachael the former FMO quarters, a three-thousand-square foot facility built by the Civilian Conservation Corps in the late 1930s. The home had a large living room, four bedrooms, a kitchen, a dining room, a laundry room, and a decent-sized backyard patio, a significant upgrade from the Mushroom Haus.

FMO quarters on Lake Wenatchee R.D. compound

With such a spacious residence for the season, Joe called the Dogman, who had completed his degree requirements at the University of Washington. He was now living with Conifer A. Coil in

Berkeley as she continued her graduate program. Since the Dogman had also been rehired for the summer as a wilderness ranger at Lake Wenatchee, Joe asked him if he was interested in renting one of the rooms in the spacious facility to share the monthly expenses. He readily agreed.

This season Raoul offered Joe a newly established position as the district's trail inspector, supervising several independent trail contractors working in the district that summer. In addition to inspecting trail contracts, Joe also functioned as a wilderness ranger and, at times, a trail dog.

A key project this season was completing a reroute of the upper Buck Creek Trail. The reroute, initiated the previous summer, remained unfinished, so Raoul prioritized the completion of the project on the popular trail. He had confidence that Joe, the Dogman, Ross, and Gottlieb, all experienced trail dogs, could finish the job in two weeks. However, the job would not be easy.

As the season progressed, it wasn't long before the FMO house became "party central" for both seasonals and permanent employees alike on the compound. The Dogman contended that their new venue was simply an upgraded version of the Mushroom Haus. Joe sought and received permission from the district ranger to move the ping-pong table from the old Lake Wenatchee Grange Hall to the FMO house. Soon, it was not uncommon to witness hotly contested ping-pong tournaments on the back porch.

Rachael spent her days caring for Zoey, and she also provided childcare services for the children of two other seasonal employees working on the compound. She maintained her interests as a master's track athlete and trained daily on the North Shore Road to compete in races in Leavenworth, Cashmere, and Wenatchee.

Meanwhile, Joe—still a member of the Plain Players—participated in the group's most ambitious endeavor to date. Carol Winters had again joined forces with Bryce Newsom, a logging contractor from Plain, to produce a dinner theater that would debut at The Cougar Inn on Lake Wenatchee.

"If successful, we will take the show on the road," predicted Winters.

The play Carol and Bryce selected—a spoof on Dudley Do-Right of the Royal Canadian Mounted Police, his girlfriend, Nell, and Snidely Whiplash, the villain—included both narrative and song-and-dance numbers. The Plain Players practiced for weeks before opening night in mid-July. Scheduled for a three-day run at the Cougar Inn, the show was an unqualified success. The Plain Players subsequently scheduled more "dinner theater" events in Leavenworth and Cashmere.

By now, the idyllic life of the late seventies had mutated to the early eighties, a "fast, strange time," as gonzo journalist Hunter S. Thompson described it. Ronald Reagan, entrenched as president, had ordered a hiring freeze for all federal agencies, which translated into bad news for Joe.

Meanwhile, Kerry had comfortably settled into the Maple Leaf neighborhood while his new love, Ashleigh, continued her law studies at Berkeley.

One weekend, Kerry popped over Stevens Pass to spend the night with Joe, Rachael, Zoey, and the Dogman in the FMO house.

"Nice digs, herring," said Kerry. "Looks like you've recovered nicely from your banishment to Entiat. You must now be back in the good graces of management."

"Yes, thanks to Raoul," replied Joe, "and perhaps the fact that the 'cazzos' are long gone," replied Joe.

"'Cazzos'?" asked Kerry.

"Yes, that's Italian for 'peckerheads,'" said Joe with a wry smile. "One retired and the other transferred to a different district."

As usual, Kerry prepared a sumptuous meal for the group; this night it was salmon barbeque with all the trimmings. Later, when Rachael put Zoey to bed, the fellows enjoyed an evening consuming various cocktails while sitting next to the fire pit on the porch, spinning tall tales about the "halcyon days of yore."

The next morning, Kerry rose early and—as a prank intended to surprise Joe—jammed a salmon head onto the empty port bottle and left it in the kitchen sink. Unfortunately for Kerry, Joe wasn't the first to come eyeball-to-eyeball with the fish face. Hearing Rachael scream, Joe ran downstairs to find Kerry's prank-gone-awry.

"Way to go, herring" said Joe to a chagrined Kerry.

"Sorry, Rachael, that wasn't intended for you," admitted a red-faced Kerry.

As the district's contract trail inspector, Joe could explore many parts of the wilderness that he had never experienced before. When Raoul informed Joe that he had received reports from hikers that the trail contractors had failed to meet the contract specifications on the Lake Minotaur trail, Joe packed a Homelite chainsaw to log out the trail properly.

The first two miles of the steep trail required most of Joe's time, as he recut many of the downed logs that obstructed hikers' passage. He would stop at each one and cut the logs to the proper distance as specified in the contract.

Those punks, Joe thought. *They won't be getting paid for this job.*

On his last cut that day, Joe pinched the saw on a large log. He struggled to free the bar but to no avail. When he ran out of time, Joe removed the engine and left the bar stuck in the log overnight.

The next morning, Joe packed another saw up the trail but discovered that the log had rolled downhill overnight, freeing the bar from the tree's unrelenting grip. Since his mission was quickly completed, Joe spent the rest of the day patrolling the basin and climbing Labyrinth Mountain above Lake Minotaur and Lake Theseus. The view from the summit offered compelling vistas of Glacier Peak and the North Cascades.

Joe spent the rest of the summer inspecting the work of trail contractors and serving as a wilderness ranger. When high hunt season began in the fall, Joe covered the Alpine Lakes Wilderness, which was designated exclusively for bow hunters. As Joe patrolled Lake Julius, Lake Donald, Loch Eileen, and Lake Ethel in his assigned territory, he developed a profound appreciation for bow hunters.

Lake Theseus from Lake Minotaur

Bow hunters are often experts in the art of stalking, using their wits to track and follow their prey, a skill that is something of a lost art. Bow hunting is the most challenging type of sport hunting. For one thing, bow hunters must draw much closer to their prey. At that point, they must release an arrow undetected and then hit a vital area of the deer. If successful, bow hunters then need to draw and quarter their game in the field to pack them out of the wilderness, no small feat.

After high hunt concluded, the Blancos prepared to depart for Eugene so that Joe could finish his final year of graduate school. Before their departure, heavy snows pounded Stevens Pass. Their trip over the pass made for a long, treacherous journey, especially with Zoey along for the ride.

Back in Eugene, Joe resumed his studies. He enrolled in the classes he felt would provide the best opportunity to qualify for a position as a public information officer for the Forest Service—his dream job. With his coursework completed, Joe's graduate advisor approved his proposed terminal project, a video presentation on minimum impact camping in the wilderness.

While Joe finished graduate school, Kerry held down the fort in Seattle, preparing a design for a remodel. He would make the occasional "milk run" down to Berkeley to see Ashleigh, stopping at various and sundry boat and sportsmen shows along the way to market his sea kayaks.

Although thoroughly absorbed in her law studies, Ashleigh would occasionally escape with Kerry for outdoor adventures during her breaks—a raft trip down the Green River in Wyoming, a kayak adventure in Barkley Sound near Vancouver Island, and a backpacking trip to the Gila Wilderness in New Mexico.

Occasionally, Kerry would meet with the Dogman and Conifer for kayak trips in popular nearby locations like Half Moon Bay and Sausalito. Conifer would often complain to Kerry about the clueless kayakers she encountered on her expeditions in and around the San Francisco Bay Area.

"By and large, these weekend urban kayakers are obnoxious," Conifer confided to Kerry disdainfully.

Displaying his trademark sarcastic wit, Kerry's response was pointed. "The assholes who come in here know nothing about the wilderness. Or the ocean. They just pull out a credit card, buy expensive gear, and consider themselves expert kayakers."

In between trips to California to see Ashleigh and kayak adventures with friends in Puget Sound, Kerry began construction on an upgrade of his Seattle home in the Maple Leaf neighborhood. He installed new doors and skylights, totally renovated the kitchen, and added French doors and a deck facing the backyard. In late October, he received a call from Joe.

"Mein herring, the Ducks are playing the Huskies on October 24," said Joe. "You up for a football game?"

"Absolutely, herring," came Kerry's reply. "But my house is a construction zone because I'm remodeling. Right now, I'm house-sitting a friend's place on Portage Bay. It's a houseboat, and I store a couple of my kayaks there. He'll be gone for the next month, so we can stay there when you come up."

"Excellent," said Joe.

Prior to the big game, Joe and his friend Lu' Moriarity rented a black Lincoln Town Car just for the occasion. They attached two flags to the side windows that read, "Go Ducks," a bold stroke considering they would be traveling behind enemy lines into the heart of Husky territory. Leaving Eugene early Saturday, they made good time up Interstate 5.

As they approached Seattle at eleven in the morning, they found that traffic had slowed to a crawl. Maneuvering the gridlock through downtown, Joe and Lu' finally found the houseboat on Portage Bay, the canal connecting Lake Union and Lake Washington adjacent to the University of Washington campus. Kerry greeted them warmly at the door, and, after a couple of beers, they paddled together in three kayaks to Husky Stadium on the opposite side of Portage Bay.

Mostly sunny and warm, it was a great day for a college football game between the two hated rivals. Duck fans, about ten thousand in attendance, helped counter cheers from the sixty thousand or so Husky fans at the stadium that day.

"Well, at least the weather is better than it was the last time I was up here," said Joe. "It's usually wet and cold, with a stiff wind blowing off Lake Washington."

"Maybe that's a good sign," Kerry noted.

The Huskies took a quick lead with a field goal and led at the end of the first quarter. In the second quarter, a Duck receiver blocked a Husky punt, resulting in a University of Oregon touchdown. At that moment, you could feel the brief Husky momentum sucked out of the stadium.

Husky fans grew quiet, and the rout was on. In the second half, the Ducks rattled off twenty-one straight points and, for all intents and purposes, the game was over. Kerry, Joe, and Lu' were high fiving each other every few minutes. Final score: Ducks 43, Huskies 19.

To celebrate the victory and perhaps rub it in, the trio hit the Blue Moon Tavern, a popular bar and music venue located near the University of Washington campus. To their great delight, jazz guitarist Pat Metheny and his band were the featured attraction that night. All three loved the up-and-coming jazz guitarist from Lee's Summit, Missouri, and his sidekick, keyboardist Lyle Mays.

After two sets and many beers, the lads reflected on the inadvertent nature of witnessing the concert of a lifetime.

"What a show!" exclaimed Lu.' "Pat Metheny is a virtuoso on the guitar."

"Yes, and Lyle Mays is a brilliant keyboardist," added Kerry. "Best show ever."

"Good thing we arrived when we did," added Joe. "We had the best seats in the house."

Basking in the glow of both a resounding Duck victory and an epic Pat Metheny concert, the boys had a nightcap on the houseboat deck and watched the lights on boats sailing back and forth through Portage Bay. The next day, Joe and Lu' cruised triumphantly south on Interstate 5 with flags flying, much to the delight of other Duck fans driving back to Oregon.

By Christmas, Ashleigh returned to Seattle with a law degree in hand. The next month, she was hired as a clerk for a judge in Anchorage. Kerry, who was ready for a change in venue, immediately proposed marriage, and Ashleigh accepted.

"Where shall we have the wedding?" asked Ashleigh.

"I suggest Leavenworth, Washington," replied Kerry. "That town has always held a special place in my heart. I know the perfect venue for an epic wedding."

The wedding site they chose was Camp Field, a Catholic Youth Organization facility complete with its quaint "Little Chapel in the Woods." Camp Field was originally home to the 983rd Company of the Civilian Conservation Corps .

Known in those days as Camp Icicle, the site housed two hundred young men during WWII. On the appointed day, Kerry and Ashleigh married among the whispering pines along the banks of the Icicle River with friends and family in attendance.

Their wedding reception would be held at the Cougar Inn on Lake Wenatchee. All the arrangements had been set with the owner well in advance. After the ceremony, the wedding party drove up the Wenatchee River through Tumwater Canyon as a caravan, arriving at Lake Wenatchee together.

Much to their chagrin, Kerry and Ashleigh received an unpleasant surprise. Arriving at the front door of the historic structure, they learned from the owners that the Cougar Inn had been closed by the Chelan County Public Health Department because of a septic system leak. Huddled outside, the wedding party suddenly had to develop an alternate plan.

Kerry, feeling a bit of angst, bellowed, "What the hell are we going to do now?"

"Don't panic, mein herring," replied Joe reassuringly. "We'll move the reception down to the Sportsman's Pub across from Parkside Grocery. Hell, we'll even bring our own musicians."

Kerry and Ashleigh had hired Jim Morningside and George Berry, a guitar duo, for the evening's entertainment. Much to their surprise, it was "Hobo Night," a themed party, at the Sportsman's Pub. The bar was packed, but the celebrants walked in undeterred. The contrast in fashion apparel between the hobos at the pub and the wedding party was stark.

Setting up their instruments in the only quiet corner of the venue, Jim and George played their blues and bluegrass classics, and the reception proceeded as planned. After their first set, one of the "hobos" in attendance approached Kerry and thanked him for providing live music. The reception continued until long after the "hobos" had retired for the evening.

"Your idea turned out to be an effective crisis management strategy, mein herring," Kerry said to Joe appreciatively.

"*Danke shoen*, mein freund," Joe replied with a wink. "After all, I'm a trained professional." Kerry simply smiled and nodded his head.

Now married and moving to Alaska with his bride, Kerry sold his house in Seattle but reinvested the equity into a mountain cabin at Snoqualmie Pass. The 1920s vintage structure was solidly built, though badly in need of improvements. Before he departed, Kerry called Joe to inform him of his move to Anchorage and his purchase of the ski cabin.

"I'm off to the Great White North with Ashleigh," said Kerry. "She already has a job as a law clerk waiting for her, and I've been hired as a project engineer at Jacobs Engineering in Anchorage. I'll miss Washington, mein herring, but I'll come down to my ski cabin from time to time to remodel, ski, and enjoy the mountains. I will be in touch, mein freund."

"Sounds good, mein herring," said Joe. "We'll be in touch."

In December, Joe's mother, Carlotta Anna Blanco, passed away after struggling for years with diabetes. While his dad had been the one to introduce him to the mountains and instill a love of the outdoors, it was Joe's mother and grandmother who raised him and helped shape the person he would become, providing moral guidance and support as he matured.

After a memorial service at Holy Family Catholic Church in Southeast Portland, Joe learned he was the beneficiary of a trust fund passed down by his grandmother when she had sold her popular Italian restaurant. A student most of his adult life, Joe had lived paycheck to paycheck. He now found himself in a better financial situation.

Following his mom's passing, Joe had come to a crossroads. Suddenly flush with cash, Joe purchased a home in Eugene near the University of Oregon campus. Then, after scouting for property near Lake Wenatchee, he purchased a building lot in Shugart Flats near Plain, Washington, intending to build a vacation home.

The property, located at the end of a county road, featured two acres of timberland, primarily Douglas fir, lodgepole pine, ponderosa pine, grand fir, and western red cedar. Situated adjacent to the junction of the Chiwawa and Wenatchee Rivers, the lot provided access to a sandy beach owned by the Chelan County Public Utility District.

During the harvest season, the local natives—the Wenatchi branch of the Yakama tribe—reportedly used this beach site to hold potlatches, or ceremonial festivals. Once the purchase agreement was signed, sealed, and delivered, Joe called Kerry to tell him the good news.

"Mein herring," Joe said, "I've probably bitten off more than I can chew. I have not only bought a home in Eugene, but I've purchased two acres of woodland near Lake Wenatchee. My hope is that someday we'll build a vacation retreat in our old stomping grounds."

"That's great news, mein herr," responded Kerry. "I'll be down to Seattle from time to time to work on the ski cabin. Let me know when you will be coming to Washington to visit your property at Lake Wenatchee."

CHAPTER TWENTY-TWO

North to Alaska

For the next two years, life was busy for both Joe and Kerry. Now happily sharing his life with Ashleigh, Kerry worked at Jacobs Engineering in Anchorage as a project manager. His position involved supervising toxic waste removal at Superfund sites in remote Alaskan sites like Dutch Harbor, Nome, and Point Barrow. He communicated with Joe by occasional letters and phone calls.

Joe and Rachael were busy having two more children to provide Zoey with company—Phoebe and Holden.

Having completed his graduate studies at the University of Oregon, Joe applied for public relations positions throughout the Pacific Northwest but wasn't having much luck. Meanwhile, the Lake Wenatchee Ranger District had offered Joe a seasonal position in its reforestation unit.

Finally, Joe applied for a position as the public relations director at a hospital in Springfield, Oregon, just across the river from Eugene. He was interviewed by Candace Barr, the director of marketing and strategic planning, and the two hit it off immediately.

"I really like the fact that you have writing experience," said Barr. "Would you be willing to submit references and come in for another interview?"

"Absolutely," replied Joe.

Joe asked his graduate school advisor and Raoul Stanford to provide references for the position at the hospital. Both offered glowing appraisals of Joe's talents and skills. At his next interview,

Barr mentioned that she would really like to hire him but asked him to submit to one more interview. Joe could tell that she might have another candidate on the line.

Feeling the pressure of the moment, Joe explained that financially, he was in a tight spot and really needed to know right then if he had the job or not. She finally agreed that a third interview was unnecessary, and he was officially hired.

"Congratulations, Joe," said Barr. "Welcome aboard."

For the next two years, Joe would work for McKenzie-Willamette, a 114-bed acute care facility, directing marketing, public relations, advertising, and fundraising initiatives for the hospital.

While Joe enjoyed his time at the hospital and learned much about health care, the intensely competitive environment required long hours on the job. Eventually, he grew weary of all the additional duties—working evenings, attending night board meetings, and on weekends, coordinating special events. He felt he was spending too much time away from Rachael and their kids, so Joe started looking for other public relations positions.

After applying for public relations jobs in the Eugene-Springfield area, Joe was hired by Eugene Water & Electric Board (EWEB), an electric, water, and steam utility in downtown Eugene. He would direct public relations activities and external communications with customers, the public, and the news media.

Now established in the field of public relations, Joe joined the Public Relations Society of America for the numerous professional development opportunities and career advancement possibilities offered by the trade organization. Just after starting his new job at EWEB, Joe was recruited by his graduate school advisor to teach public relations classes as a part-time instructor at UO while working full-time at the utility.

Both Joe and Kerry now seemed set professionally; both had found meaningful positions in their chosen fields. During Kerry's occasional trips to Seattle for business, Joe would drive north and meet with him at his Snoqualmie Pass cabin. But then, because they were so busy, the two friends fell out of touch for a period of time. Eventually, Joe learned through the grapevine that Ashleigh and Kerry had divorced. Concerned about his friend after hearing about the end of his marriage, Joe called Kerry to provide support.

From experience, Joe surmised that Kerry's emotional state would be fragile after yet another broken relationship. Joe suggested a weeklong backpacking excursion along the PCT to help Kerry clear his head.

"I know you're going over a rough patch of road right now, mein herring," said Joe. "I heard about your breakup with Ashleigh. Let's meet at my property in Shugart Flats, drive to Stevens Pass, and hike the PCT to your cabin at Snoqualmie Pass."

"I like the idea, mein herr," Kerry responded. "I could use a break from Anchorage right now. Let's meet in two weeks."

"Excellent," replied Joe. "So, what happened with you and Ashleigh?"

"I don't know for sure, herring," replied Kerry. "Before we were married, everything was perfect. We both loved adventure, and we both loved to ski. But after the wedding, she changed. Or maybe I changed. Or maybe we both changed. For example, it would snow several inches that night, resulting in a perfect powder day the next morning. But instead of skiing, she'd rather we spend our time shopping for new bathroom tiles.

"Perhaps I was not tending to the garden of my wife's best interests and needs, or mine neither," continued Kerry. "But the divorce itself was quite amicable, all settled over a Sunday breakfast. We simply decided it was best to pursue our dreams separately."

"Well, I'm relieved to hear you've come to terms with your breakup, herring," said Joe. "I can imagine it could be painful."

"For better or worse, it happened," said Kerry. "For me, there's still more to experience as part of my healing process, or whatever one calls it. Thanks again for always being there for me."

Two weeks later, Joe arrived in Shugart Flats and began to prepare for an extended hike with Kerry on the PCT. At this point,

Joe had moved a travel trailer onto the property and built a shed for protection from the deep winter snows. He also employed his friend and neighbor Flynn Stein to build a well house, complete with a shower and sauna.

While waiting for Kerry to arrive, Joe also ordered a port-a-potty from Apple Valley Waste Disposal in Wenatchee.

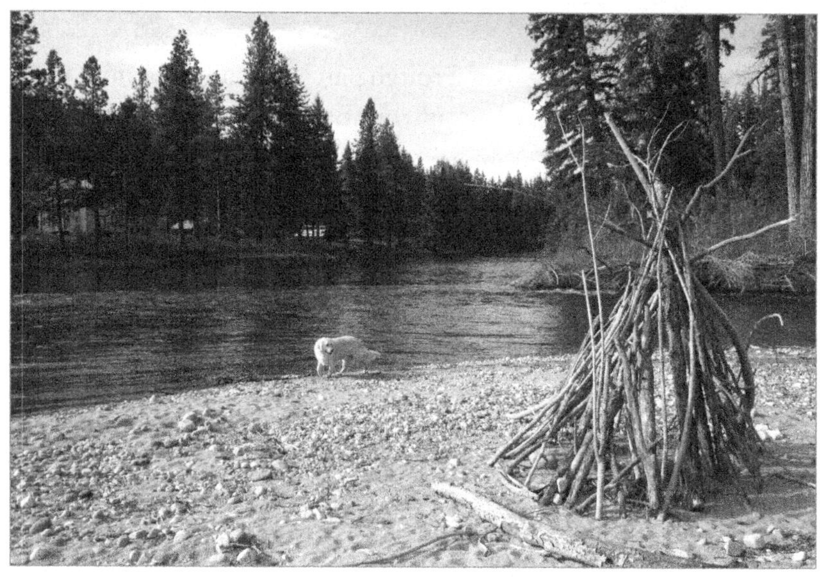

The beach at the bottom of Shugart Flats property

Once he arrived at the end of the road in Shugart Flats, Kerry wheeled around the school bus turnaround and rolled down his window. He could see the image of someone through the trees and so he yelled out, "I think I'm lost."

"Well, then, you must be in the right place," replied Joe as he approached Kerry. "Welcome to Base Camp One."

Both laughed and hugged.

"So good to see you, mein freund," said Joe. "How are you feeling?'

"Much better now that I'm here," replied Kerry.

After a couple of days of rest and repose at the Shugart Flats property, Kerry and Joe departed for their trek along the PCT, the

2,653-mile national scenic route designated in 1968. They stopped briefly at the Squirrel Tree Inn at Cole's Corner to have breakfast, then drove up US Highway 2 toward Stevens Pass.

Joe parked his Toyota Highlander (a "golf cart on steroids," according to Kerry), and they began their hike through the Stevens Pass Ski Area over the ridge to the upper Mill Creek Valley. They crossed under the 115 kV power lines from Rocky Reach Dam north of Wenatchee, which provide the electrical lifeblood for Seattle and its vicinity, and it didn't take long for trouble to develop.

After less than a mile, the Vibram sole from Joe's left boot detached completely as they crossed the upper part of Mill Creek. Joe had only worn the two-hundred-dollar hiking boots a couple of dozen times. Despite the loss of the sole, the boot seemed salvageable. Joe felt he should just pack them out and hike in his camp shoes for the remainder of the trip.

"Why don't you leave them here and come back later?" Kerry suggested.

"Nah," Joe replied, "I'll just pack them out. But REI is going to hear about these boots. I will want a new pair or a refund."

Shortly after crossing Mill Creek, they passed the boundary sign for the Alpine Lakes Wilderness. Joe looked forward to hiking this stretch of the PCT ever since he worked on the Alpine Lakes Planning Team at the Mt. Baker-Snoqualmie National Forest Supervisor's Office in Seattle. The 394,000-acre wilderness derives its name from the nearly seven hundred jewel-like lakes nestled among the high rock peaks and timbered valleys of the region.

After a delightful trek of twelve miles on the first day, they noticed that a Pacific storm with the potential for lightning had moved into the region, so Kerry and Joe established camp at Trap Lake and called it a day. Setting up their tent, they rolled out their sleeping bags and popped a couple of ibuprofens as the storm settled in. The next morning, they awoke in a chilly cloud.

"I like this fog," announced Joe, as he sipped a cup of hot coffee. "It's reassuring."

"Yes, mein herring," agreed Kerry. "It means we'll have a great day for hiking, temperature-wise. Once the fog lifts, it should be warm and sunny."

Once they were through the pass at Surprise Gap, the weather improved, with flashes of sunlight peeking through the clouds as they descended to Deception Lake. They paused for lunch by a beautiful rocky stream resplendent with yellow asters. Joe's camp shoes had held up well, and though traction was lacking, they were more comfortable than his damaged boots.

Fortunately, the terrain had accommodated Joe's less-than-acceptable shoes for now. As they contoured south on the ridge leading to Deception Pass, the trail was soft from the subalpine forest. The view of Marmot Lake resting in a huge mountain cirque across the wide valley was stunning.

But Joe's luck with his camp shoes finally ran out at the Daniel Creek crossing. The climb to Cathedral Pass was steep and rocky. Joe hit the deck several times to avoid rolling an ankle. The steep climb made for difficult walking in tennis shoes. Joe's pace slowed. Kerry got further ahead, which weighed on his mind until Joe encountered two women hikers who assured him that Kerry had established camp and was waiting for him a mere quarter mile away.

Their assurances put some spring in his step. Joe arrived at the pass just below Cathedral Rock to find Kerry preparing dinner. The spot was mystical, with numerous campsites and a sandy beach on a mellifluous creek. Just as Joe arrived, another couple leaving the campsite mentioned that the camp was indeed a magical spot.

"This stream is flowing vigorously right now, but the water will vanish completely by morning," said one of the women.

"You're kidding," responded Joe.

"Just wait and see," said the woman.

That evening, Joe snuggled in his sleeping bag immediately adjacent to the babbling creek. As he dozed, Joe clearly heard melodies in the sounds of that creek, ranging from classical, jazz, and even a bit of what he swore was Led Zeppelin. Later that night, Joe was awakened, not by noises, but by utter and total silence; he could no longer hear the creek. Puzzled but too exhausted even to peek outside his tent, he drifted back into a deep slumber.

Cathedral Rock from Cathedral Creek

The next morning, Joe could hardly believe his eyes. The delightfully melodic stream known as Cathedral Creek had totally vanished! The stream bed and little sandy beach were still there, but not a lick of water remained.

"Now that's something you don't see every day," said Joe. "The creek bed that was heartily flowing yesterday is now a dry creek bed."

Gazing up the slope toward the summit of Cathedral Rock, Kerry noticed a large snowfield near the top of the draw.

"There's your water source for the creek, mein herring," observed Kerry. "The snowfield melts during the daylight hours, then refreezes at night when the temperature dips."

After a quick breakfast of energy bars, Kerry and Joe packed up their camp and continued down the trail toward Snoqualmie Pass. The day before, the pair had met northbound hikers who mentioned rumors of a manhunt ahead on the PCT, though few had any specifics. More passing hikers that morning confirmed these reports.

Word on the trail was that a twenty-mile section of the PCT was now closed due to the manhunt and an alternative route established. Wilderness rangers patrolled PCT access points to make sure that hikers used the detour. Nonplussed, Kerry and Joe continued south through Cathedral Pass where they witnessed incredible views of Cathedral Rock.

More passing hikers informed Joe and Kerry that a wilderness ranger was stationed farther down the trail to reroute hikers around the area where police were conducting their manhunt. Sure enough, a wilderness ranger waiting for southbound hikers at the next trail junction down Spinola Creek told them to detour to Waptus Lake.

The detour would then lead over Waptus Pass, down to the Pete Lake Trail, and out to the road at Cooper Lake. After another fifteen miles of Forest Service road to the Mineral Creek Trailhead, the detour connected back with the PCT about twelve miles north of Snoqualmie Pass.

As Kerry and Joe conferred with the wilderness ranger over a set of maps, Joe asked him if he could convince the Cle Elum Ranger District dispatcher to place a phone call for him to arrange for transportation. "Certainly," the ranger replied.

Joe had the ranger relay a message to his friend Randy Wilson—now the FMO on the Leavenworth Ranger District—to pick them up at the Pete Lake Trailhead at Cooper Lake.

The reply came swiftly. Randy would rendezvous with Joe and Kerry at Cooper Lake. Kerry and Joe followed the detour down Spinola Creek to Waptus Lake, crossed the Waptus River, and climbed the numerous switchbacks up to Waptus Pass, where they established their camp for the night.

As they woke in the predawn light, a variety of birds broke into song—each chirping its own tune in concert with the other, with percussion provided by a woodpecker—a wondrous melody. By the time the sun had lit the pass, the concert was over.

Joe and Kerry packed camp and bade farewell to Shootout, another PCT hiker who shared their campsite in Waptus Pass. Most long-range hikers on the PCT adopt pseudonyms during their trek. Examples included Banshee, Salty, Two Shoes, Blister Butt, Flicker, Muleskinner, Ice Cap, Freebee, Moondog and Mr. Zip. Kerry and Joe had adopted Midwochen and Laslo, respectively, as their PCT pseudonyms.

With renewed vigor, they hiked down toward Pete Lake from Waptus Pass. Though they enjoyed their hike on the PCT, they were nonetheless anxious to emerge from the wilderness. Now on a flat trail, their pace quickened. Knowing Randy's propensity for punctuality, Kerry and Joe arrived at the Pete Lake Trailhead at Cooper Lake an hour early.

Randy wheeled in at a quarter past one in the afternoon, rolled down his window, and asked, "Anybody need a ride?"

"Boy, are you a sight for sore feet," Joe replied.

For Kerry and Joe, it was time to "head for the barn" back to Shugart Flats.

CHAPTER TWENTY-THREE

Das Tree Haus

Less than six months after his divorce from Ashleigh had been finalized, Kerry had inexplicably eloped with Carmina Angeles, a divorcée from Anchorage. Kerry met her on one of his many kayaking excursions with groups of friends. The newlyweds had held their "official" wedding ceremony in the Grand Canyon as they kayaked with a flotilla down the Colorado River.

Life had once again become idyllic for Kerry as the newlyweds settled into Carmina's home on a hillside in Anchorage. While Kerry was hired as a site mitigation engineer for the Alyeska Corporation, Carmina worked for the City of Anchorage.

For Kerry, marrying Carmina included a bonus: her children and grandchildren from her previous marriages. Kerry now had a ready-made family, which picked up his spirits immensely. He had always admired Joe for having the ability to persevere in having a family.

Eventually purchasing a sailboat, Kerry and Carmina took many trips and adventures throughout the Pacific coast islands of Alaska, Canada, and Washington. When Carmina heard that the 14th Dalai Lama, on a visit to the US, would stop in Eugene, she insisted that they make the pilgrimage to Oregon.

They stayed with Joe and Rachael and attended the Dalai Lama's presentation and all the related festivities surrounding his appearance. Out for a beer at a campus pub, Joe asked Kerry if he was in good spirits.

"Yes, mein herring," replied Kerry. "My life is on the upswing."

"Your marriage to Carmina was rather sudden, wasn't it?" Joe inquired discreetly.

"Funny you should ask, herring," said Kerry. "Her previous husband was a friend of mine. He predicted that I would become her next target.'"

"Seriously?" responded Joe.

"*Jawohl*," replied Kerry. "Our wedding was quite spontaneous, and I was vulnerable after my divorce from Ashleigh. I just kind of went with the flow and it seems to have worked out."

Back in Anchorage, Kerry and Carmina settled in and worked at their respective jobs, with Kerry out "on assignment" in far-flung locations such as the North Slope. Carmina held down the fort with some of her family nearby. On occasion, Kerry and Carmina would travel to Michigan to visit her parents. Well known for his talents as "the trip master," Kerry would take her father hunting in the north woods of Michigan. Kerry had apparently regained his equilibrium.

A couple of months later, Joe called Kerry to inform him of his next junket north to Washington.

"Mein herr, I have a public relations conference coming up in April in Seattle," said Joe. "I can take extra time off so that we can make the sojourn over Stevens Pass to our property near Plain. Tell you what, I'll pick you up in Seattle on April 22."

"It's a date, mein herring," concluded Kerry. "Like I always say, 'if it ain't on the calendar, it ain't gonna happen.'"

Picking up Kerry at a friend's house in West Seattle, Joe immediately drove northwest to US Highway 2 in Monroe and proceeded east through Sultan, Startup, Gold Bar, Baring, and Skykomish to Stevens Pass and then down to the Lake Wenatchee turnoff to Plain just past the 59er Diner, a popular roadside attraction where every waitress is known as "Flo."

When they arrived in Shugart Flats, Kerry inspected the two-acre site. Amazed, he observed the stunning vistas of Icicle Ridge, Entiat Ridge, and Natapoc Mountain. Looking north, he could see the edge of the property sloping down to a sandy beach at the junction of the Chiwawa and Wenatchee Rivers.

"This must be the center of the known universe; it's perfect," Kerry gushed. "What are your plans, mein herring?"

"We purchased this particular property because of its secluded locale, mein freund," Joe replied. "We're centrally located here in terms of the wilderness. On the south, we have the Alpine Lakes Wilderness and on the north the Glacier Peak Wilderness. To the west, we have easy access to Seattle. Plus, the price was right: fifteen thousand dollars for two acres."

"Do you plan to build?" Kerry continued.

"Yes, eventually, mein herring," Joe responded. "But for now, it's a base camp for wilderness adventures. We'll use this travel trailer for the time being. I'd like to build a tree fort for the kids and, later, perhaps a rustic yet elaborate hacienda."

"Tree fort?" Kerry asked. "How about a tree house? You know, like a tiny house in a tree? You have three mature Douglas firs on the edge of the slope that would be perfect!"

Kerry explained to Joe that "tiny homes" were a new craze sweeping the United States, with some homeowners even locating their small structures in trees. The movement, he said, was initiated by people who were looking for something different than gigantic—and overpriced—retirement homes that have come to dominate much of America.

"Who on earth would willingly live in a tiny shack?" Joe replied. "That sounds horrible at worst and cramped at best."

"I know what you're thinking, mein herring," countered Kerry reassuringly. "That's where you're wrong. These tiny houses can be as luxurious as your normal-sized home with less than half the space and at a fraction of the cost."

Noting Joe's skeptical expression, Kerry continued. "We're not talking 'shack' here. These are high-quality tiny homes, and the people buying them are not just from one demographic either. The tiny house movement includes young people, newlyweds, and even retirees. Intrigued? I'll send you more information in a week or two."

"I don't know if my finances can handle a building project right now, herring," countered Joe. "I have a wife and three kids, two mortgages, and a dog. We might want to hold off on incurring any more expenses."

"Tell you what, herring" suggested Kerry. "Let's put in the platform, at my expense, and then we can figure out where to go from there. Perhaps we can scale back our expectations a bit and let the process develop over time."

"Okay," said Joe. "That sounds reasonable. I do like the idea of the location for a tree house."

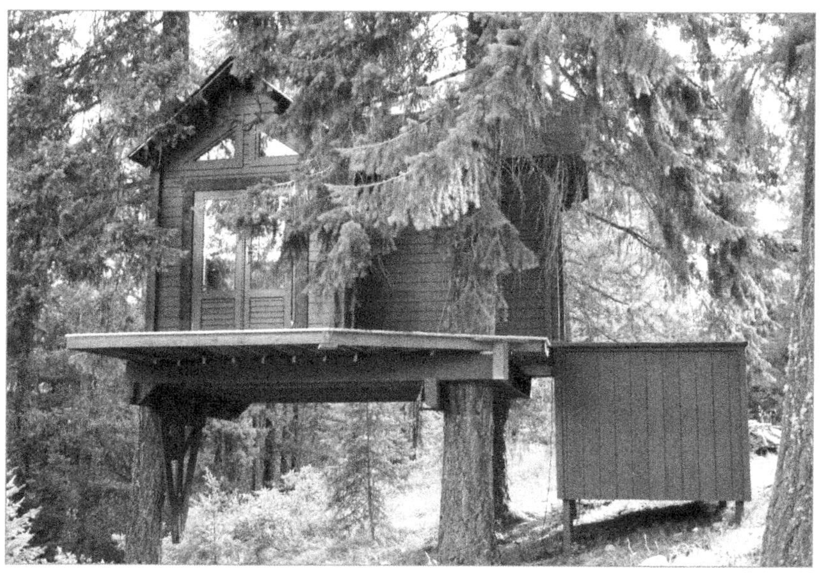

Das Tree Haus at the Owl Conservatory

As they walked the property line gathering information and perspectives on the proposed tree house, Joe stumbled onto an inflatable owl—likely a scarecrow that had been used to protect fruits and vegetables in someone's garden—that had deflated in the tall grass.

Observing the decoy, Kerry laughed. "It's a sign, Dr. Gonzo." said Kerry. "You should call this place the Owl Farm."

"Nice idea, herring," Joe replied. "I like the connection to Hunter S. Thompson's lair in Woody Creek, but I prefer 'Owl Conservatory.' After all, we're not farming owls here. We're providing sanctuary for owls, and there's a direct link with our time working with 'Hannah's Hooters.'"

"And so it is," concluded Kerry. "The Owl Conservatory."

After two more days at the "Center of the Known Universe," Kerry and Joe drove back to Seattle for Joe's conference. Arriving at the Crowne Plaza Hotel, Kerry was surprised to learn that Joe had rented the entire penthouse suite at the exclusive five-star facility. The suite had 360-degree views of urban Seattle, Elliott Bay, and the Olympic Mountains. It had two spacious bedrooms, a kitchen, and a living room.

"How can you swing this kind of spread, mein herring?" asked Kerry.

"Perks of a career as a public relations practitioner, Mr. Vallindaklopf," replied Joe with a grin.

"Mein herring, I must say I'm envious of your success in this racket you refer to as 'journalism' and 'public relations'—the miserable excuse you have made for yourself for a means of livelihood," Kerry observed with a hint of sarcasm. "I'm just surprised you didn't consider a career as a fruit scientist."

They both laughed heartily at Kerry's reference to their past.

"Herring, to start these conferences, the Public Relations Society of America sponsors a hosted bar with hors d'oeuvres and whatnot," said Joe. "You in?"

"A hosted bar?" replied Kerry. "Say no more."

Arriving at the reception, Kerry was impressed with the mixer event. Many attendees were attractive, well-dressed, and articulate women. As they consumed the high-priced fare and an abundant number of rum and Cokes, Joe and Kerry worked the room like professionals.

After socializing for a while, Kerry confided to Joe. "I take it all back, herring. You did indeed choose the right profession."

"Helmut, talking to one of my colleagues, I just heard that Dire Straits will play the Seattle Center tomorrow night," said Joe. "The woman I talked to said they've been sold out for weeks, but we still might be able to get tickets if we show up outside the arena."

"I'll work on it tomorrow while you attend your conference," replied Kerry.

"Sounds good," said Joe.

At the time, Dire Straits was one of the hottest rock and roll bands in the world, playing to sold-out stadiums around the world. Both Joe and Kerry were huge fans. Catching Dire Straits would be a big deal and quite unexpected considering that they hadn't even heard of the show until now.

The next morning, Joe attended the various professional development sessions at the hotel while Kerry kicked around downtown Seattle, hitting the Pike Place Market and the ticket office at the Seattle Center, site of the 1962 World's Fair.

At the end of the day, Joe met Kerry in the hotel bar.

"Guess what, Gonzo," queried Kerry. "I've secured two tickets to Dire Straits."

"That's great!" replied Joe incredulously. "I thought they were sold out."

"They were," said Kerry, "but they had a few tickets that people had returned. We have two seats in the ninth row."

"Outstanding!" exclaimed Joe.

Kerry and Joe attended the concert that night and then parted ways the next morning. Kerry caught his flight to Anchorage, and Joe drove back down I-5 to Eugene.

A month later, Kerry sent a letter to Joe to provide an update on his planning endeavors related to the tree house.

Herring:

I am onto something new in design. It's a fabric structure that's extremely durable and can be used year-round (it has a stove). You can set it up and take it down without too much difficulty. It's basically an all-weather tent designed to perfectly fit the platform.

As you may recall, I also intend to build a small shed adjacent to the platform, which will be attached to the three Douglas firs. The fabric unit will fit seamlessly right onto the platform. The deck would have a clear, durable roof like those found in greenhouses.

The result will be the existing platform and an adjacent screened deck/porch. The fabric unit would only be necessary when people needed it. You could sleep on the porch in the warmer months and in the fabric structure with the stove during the cooler months.

The advantages are that the fabric structure would be cheaper, more modular, and plenty durable. Plus, it would not become a target for curious county inspectors. It ain't a teepee, it ain't a yurt, and it ain't really a tent, but it is awesome. We will let the idea gestate for a while.

Love, Kerry

That spring, construction began on the platform, or superstructure, to provide a surface for the fabric tent. When he had time, Joe would help Kerry with construction activities related to the platform, installing two platform joists that ran east and west and one joist running north and south.

One day, as the two of them labored on the platform, Kerry attempted to drill a hole high in one of the Douglas firs to install an anchor bolt. He was holding the tool too tightly, and the drill suddenly jammed, spinning him around like a pinwheel until he flew off the ladder into a patch of ceanothus bushes. Landing hard, Kerry just dusted himself off and moved on to the next anchor. Such was his luck.

"Herring," said Joe, "you know just enough about construction to be dangerous."

Nonplussed, Kerry simply shrugged his shoulders and continued drilling.

Later that summer, Kerry had an epiphany. Instead of an all-weather tent, why not build a tiny home on the platform? He researched classes on how to build tiny homes and enrolled in a seminar conducted at the University of Washington. He came away excited about his new plan and fired off a missive to Joe:

Mein herring:

Some updated and exciting information to share with you. I just completed a class on building tiny homes, and I've found a vendor who produces high-quality structures called Yeti Log Cabins—these small stick-built cabins are very reasonably priced.

The Yeti Log Cabin kits are cut in the Baltics, where they have seven mills churning them out. Then, I thought, why not just order the ten-by-twelve, which is cheaper than the larger models and costs less to ship. I let the architect, who serves as the East Coast distributor of Yeti Log Cabins, know of my decision.

The architect called back in less than an hour. She said that Yeti is so excited about the idea of installing a tiny home as a tree house that she would give me the whole kit for a substantial discount and send a contractor to help assemble the structure quickly. I saved a few thousand bucks on the deal and placed the order. As a bonus, she said she would throw in a smaller tiny home to install on the property. Kits will arrive in August.

Plus, there's more good news. I've really connected well with the project architect, Olga Egovora. She said my construction management skills are perfect for Yeti. She holds the North American rights as an exclusive dealer for Yeti products.

The kits, ranging from garden huts to full-scale residential homes, are selling like crazy in Europe and Russia. They're fully permitted and comply with local codes. Olga and I are well into conversations about a new role for me as the offi-

cial Yeti area representative for Oregon, Washington, and Alaska. Mein herr, this could be my future part-time career, starting with the tree cabin at the Owl Conservatory.

I will sign on with Yeti within the next week or two. Hey, a part-time job as Yeti's area representative? I'm shocked—shocked, I tell you. I would be in "on the ground floor" on a new trend, as they say, and I'd get a cut of everything.

I am flying to Baltimore next week for meetings with Olga to develop a strategy for marketing the cabins. Shortly after that, I'll travel to Lithuania with her to get the total rundown and determine how to make it work in North America.

Your thoughts, at your convenience, mein herring.

Love, Kerry

As Joe considered the fast-moving developments related to the prospect of building a tree house on the Owl Conservatory, he readily admitted that while his kids were too young to have asked him to build them a tree house, he was growing increasingly enamored with the idea, thanks to Kerry's enthusiasm.

Joe wanted to do what every grown man secretly wants to do—construct an arboreal retreat. For now, he was going to roll with the notion and rely on Kerry's spirit and stamina.

Over the winter, Kerry traveled to Lithuania with Olga to secure two tiny home kits, and initiate transport to Seattle. By spring, the kits were delivered to the Owl Conservatory. With Joe's help, and with assistance from Kerry's wide spectrum of friends, construction began in the spring.

First, they erected four walls with windows and sheer panels, along with preprimed and painted siding and a gabled roof to allow for two lofts on either end for sleeping and gear. By September, "Das Tree Haus," as Kerry liked to call it, was starting to look like the real thing.

Kerry's longtime friend Rick Oldman helped construct an adjacent storage unit and connect it to the platform. Then, it was on to the second kit. Kerry enlisted Flynn Stein to help construct the smaller structure, which Joe promptly dubbed *Capanna Montagna* ("mountain hut" in Italian).

The smaller structure was reminiscent of the 1,300 mountain huts that dot the Alps across eight European countries from Switzerland, Germany, and France in the west, to Austria, Liechtenstein, and Slovenia in the east, to Italy and Monaco in the south.

Capanna Montagna at the Owl Conservatory

In retrospect, the entire project resembled a science project, yet it was also totally organic. Building a tree house required both left-brain characteristics such as logic, critical thinking, and numbers and right-brained traits such as intuition, creativity, and visual imaging.

Admiring the completed construction projects, Kerry told Joe that it was a "good thing we had two heads on this project."

"Yeah," replied Joe with a wry grin, "which means that between the two of us, we claim to have a whole brain."

CHAPTER TWENTY-FOUR

Lost in the Labyrinth

The next season, Kerry and Joe organized a group of compadres from the days of yore on the Lake Wenatchee Ranger District to meet at the Owl Conservatory to help with the finish work on the cabins and go for a hike into the wilderness. Besides early fall, the next best time for hiking is late spring before the flying pests have reappeared.

And so, it was. A small cadre from that loosely knit consortium known as the Aldo Leopold Society applied the final touches to the new tiny homes, including painting, adding trim work, and installing metal roofs on both structures. Once the work was completed, the group embarked on a journey into the backcountry.

This odyssey would transport the former rangers into a familiar realm of Greek mythology: Lake Minotaur, Labyrinth Mountain, and Lake Theseus in the upper reaches of the Little Wenatchee River drainage.

As the group hiked up the precipitous first two miles of the trail, Kerry inquired, "Who named these features? Sylvester?"

"Yep," replied Joe. "Puzzled by the odd contours of the terrain, A.H. Sylvester, the first forest supervisor on the Wenatchee National Forest, likened the area to a story from Greek mythology."

Joe continued, "As the story goes, the Minotaur, a fearsome beast with the head of a bull and the body of a man, had been banished by King Minos of Corinth to a huge maze known as the Labyrinth. The Minotaur remained imprisoned in the maze, receiving annual offerings of Athenian youth to devour in tribute to King Minos."

Lake Minotaur and Labyrinth Mountain

"One such youth, Theseus, son of King Aegeus of Athens, volunteered for the hazardous assignment of traveling to Crete to slay the Minotaur and end the sacrificial deaths of young Athenians."

Joe continued. "When Theseus reached Crete, the daughters of King Minos immediately fell in love with him. They provided the Athenian with the key to escaping the Labyrinth: a ball of string to have the ability to retrace his steps," concluded Joe.

"Where did you learn this?" asked Kerry.

"I took a Greek mythology class at the university," replied Joe. "It was fascinating stuff."

"What happed to Theseus?" asked Gottlieb.

"Finding the Minotaur in a far corner of the Labyrinth, Theseus killed the fearsome man-beast with a sword, and, discovering other

Athenians held as captives, he led the group out of the Labyrinth," Joe concluded.

Back at the Owl Conservatory after the hike, Kerry pulled Joe aside and confided in him. "Truth be told, I am battling my own demons, mein herring," said Kerry. "I have fallen into a labyrinth of despair."

"What?" asked Joe.

"Sorry I haven't told you sooner, but Carmina has unceremoniously dumped me. I'm on my own once again," said Kerry, admitting that he had plunged into a mental abyss. With no place to go, he had agonized over his situation and stayed with friends for several weeks until he could decide what to do.

"What happened?" asked Joe.

"Our partnership, as it turns out, had cracks in the foundation," Kerry replied. "I was vulnerable after my divorce from Ashleigh, and she took advantage of the situation. I married too quickly. Later, I learned she wasn't completely truthful and honest with me about what I assumed were mutual goals and shared financial resources."

"Ultimately, I confronted her," Kerry continued, "and the relationship began to unravel. I thought our plan was to live in Alaska while we remodeled my cabin at Snoqualmie Pass and travel the world. That dream has gone up in smoke now. It got pretty weird. I've been kicked out of 'her' home."

"What are you going to do now?" Joe asked.

"I'm going to move to Snoqualmie Pass and buy a new sailboat that I can moor at the Edmonds Marina just north of Seattle," said Kerry. "I have been in touch with Bob and Ada Rourke at High Camp, and they've offered me a job as an expedition guide."

"Excellent, mein herr," said Joe. "That is the perfect gig work for the likes of you."

Joe knew the story of Bob and Ada Rourke and the Alpine Lakes High Camp very well. The couple were members of the Mountaineers, a climbing club based in Seattle, and they spent many weekends hiking and skiing near Leavenworth. They fell in love with the Enchantment Lakes Basin high in the Wenatchee Range of the Cascades.

Later, Bob, an engineer at Boeing for twenty years, took early retirement. The couple sold their home near Seattle and moved to Leavenworth, where they founded "Family Adventures," an outfitter providing camping experiences in the Alpine Lakes Wilderness.

Once the Alpine Lakes Wilderness Area was formally established, the Rourkes could no longer take paying customers into the Enchantments. Considering their alternatives, they learned they could lease land from a timber company for the purpose of providing outfitter services, so they established the Scottish Lakes Nomad Camp near Lake Wenatchee. They built platforms for tents and led guided ski touring expeditions in the winter and hikes in the summer.

In late July, Kerry suggested that Joe join him for a raft trip either down the Colorado River or the Middle Fork of the Salmon River. As he considered Kerry's proposal, Joe realized he had lived in Oregon most of his life but had never rafted the Rogue River, known as one of the best whitewater trips in the West.

"Those trips would be delightful," Joe said to Kerry. "What do you think about floating the Rogue River instead? We could pick up Paul Kirchmeier in Corvallis and take a multi-day float on the wild and scenic river. It's virtually all wilderness."

"That sounds great, mein herring," said Kerry. "I know several outfitters, and I'll line something up for us."

Kerry called Rogue River Journeys, an outfitter based in Bayside, California. They had three openings in early August, so Kerry immediately booked a trip and plunked down a deposit to reserve their spots. After coordinating their itinerary, Kerry, Joe and Paul made plans to arrive in Galice, Oregon, on August 11. The raft trip would become the experience of a lifetime.

The Rogue River, known for its salmon runs, whitewater boating, and rugged wilderness, was one of the original eight rivers named in the federal Wild and Scenic Rivers Act in 1968.

From its source at Boundary Springs in Crater Lake National Park, the Rogue River flows two hundred fifteen miles through the younger High Cascades and the older Western Cascades, another volcanic province. Continuing west, the Rogue River breaches the even more ancient Klamath Mountains before flowing into the Pacific Ocean at Gold Beach.

On the appointed day, the threesome departed for the three-hour drive from Eugene to Galice. They had booked a room at the Galice Resort, their rendezvous point with the outfitter. The rustic establishment had a restaurant, and, more importantly, a bar.

Galice Resort Lodge

That night they spent a couple of hours in the bar and met another participant in the Rogue River float, Roxy Perot. A California resident, Roxy was charming, and she seemed enamored with Kerry. Still seriously smarting from his impending divorce from Carmina Angeles, Kerry later mentioned to Joe and Paul that he "must get to know her better."

"Good idea, herring," replied Joe. "After all, Roxy had readily agreed when Paul hilariously told her that the three of us were fun and interesting people."

The next morning, the group met Bo Wentz and four other river guides employed by Rogue River Journeys for this trip. A professor of forestry at the University of Montana in Missoula, Bo had spent many summers as a river guide on numerous waterways in the Western US.

After breakfast at Galice Resort and a prelaunch meeting with the twenty other participants, the group proceeded to Argo Launch, less than two miles above the wilderness section of the Rogue River. Joe and Paul jumped into the raft with Bo, and Kerry launched his hard-shell kayak. The flotilla included five large rafts, a half-dozen inflatable kayaks, and about a dozen hard-shell kayaks.

Once participants had wrapped their gear into dry bags, the guides demonstrated how to rescue "swimmers" who happen to fall out of a boat. The river was mellow at first, but it didn't take long to reach a Class III rapid at Grave Creek.

Further down the river at Rainey Falls, most of the boaters portaged around the rough stuff, but a couple of the hard-shell kayakers braved the churning rapids like the experienced pros they were. Arriving at Tyee Bar to establish their first camp, Joe was feeling elated from the day's experience.

"What a pleasant day in a raft," Joe told Kerry. "The sun beating down on us, and the splash water providing a refreshing interlude through the riffles and rapids. Just awesome."

"I figured you'd enjoy a float like this, mein herring," Kerry replied.

After disembarking, the guides established a shady spot on the beach with tarps and oars. They then distributed cold beer and soda to all the participants. Unloading the rafts, the guides constructed a makeshift kitchen and began preparations for dinner while the rafters and kayakers pulled gear from their dry bags and started setting up their tents.

Relaxing with a cold beer, Joe reflected, "I almost feel guilty, with those folks doing all the serious work."

"Yes, and in case anybody is wondering, the operative word there is 'almost,'" replied Kerry with a laugh.

Breaking camp the next morning after a sumptuous breakfast of eggs, bacon, hashbrowns, and copious amounts of coffee, they began Day Two on the river with a bang. A couple of inflatable kayakers dumped their boats in Wildcat Rapids, a Class III riffle that will flip kayaks that turn sideways. Joe's raft was closest to the "swimmers," so he and Paul employed their newly acquired rescue skills.

After a successful rescue, Joe told Paul, "That was great. I've never felt so valued as a human being."

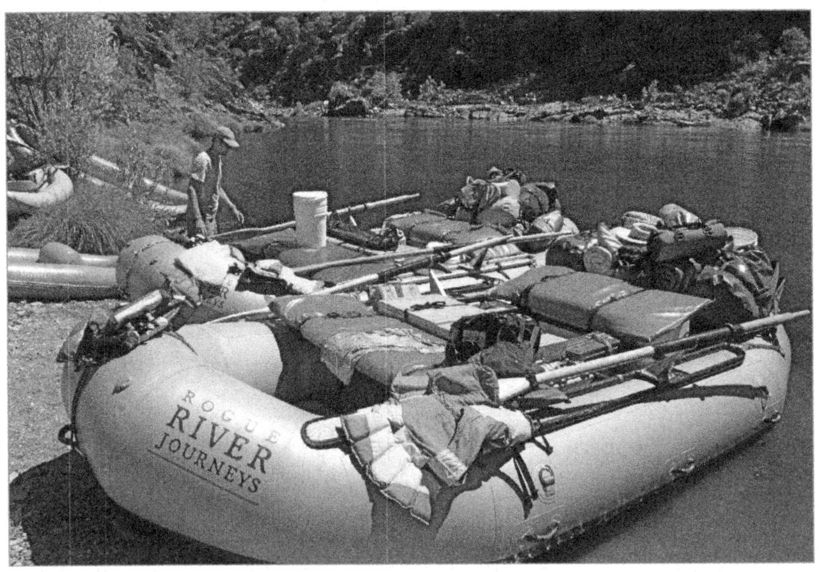

Break time on the Rogue River

After Wildcat Rapids, the group passed through a succession of rapids with colorful names such as Quiz Show, Slim Pickens, and Kelsey Chutes, then stopped for a break at the Zane Grey cabin. An American author, Grey was best known for his adventure stories of an idealized image of the American West, novels which became even more popular with the advent of television.

Grey, who built the cabin in 1926, penned *Riders of the Purple Sage* and other books adapted for television, such as the *Lone Ranger* and *Sgt. Preston of the Yukon*. In addition to his cabin on the Rogue River, Grey—an avid fisherman—maintained rustic residences in Florida, Arizona, and on Catalina Island. Grey utilized his Rogue River hideaway, a simple one-room cabin of peeled logs and hand-split shingles, as a frequent retreat until 1936.

The group's next camp was Missouri Bar. Thanks to the epicurean skills of the river guides, one and all dined like royalty. Unfortunately, the area was rife with poison oak, and Joe and Paul were exposed. That night, the group witnessed a Perseid meteor shower, with stars shooting in every direction against a blackened sky.

On Day Three, the flotilla stopped by the Rogue River Ranch, a pioneer farming complex. Nestled in the heart of the wild section of the Rogue River at its junction with Mule Creek, the ranch evolved as a gold-mining community, with as many as one hundred residents trying to scratch a living from the river. The ranch is now a National Historic Site.

"Now this is what you call remote!" announced Paul.

After the Rogue River Ranch, the expedition entered Mule Creek Canyon. Seemingly otherworldly, the canyon featured vertical rock walls that create strange currents and broils. Without much room to maneuver, it took real skill to avoid slamming into the sides of each wall.

"We don't want to go sideways in this stretch!" shouted Kerry to the others as he scouted ahead.

Mule Creek Canyon also included rapids called Jaws and Coffee Pot. Next up was Blossom Bar, a Class IV rapid, which has a storied history. Early settlers in the area named it for the lush azaleas that decorate the canyon. Located at the mouth of two steep drainages with an abundance of boulders that clog the river, Blossom Bar was the most difficult whitewater in the wild and scenic section of the Rogue River.

Even though a scout boat piloted by one of the guides paddled ahead to check for campsites, the group got "squinked" and had to settle for a campsite known as "Last Chance" below Tacoma Rapids. In river parlance, "squinked" meant that another party had already claimed their planned campsite. That evening—their last on the river—the guides conducted an interactive wine-tasting activity, enjoyed by one and all.

"Isn't it amazing how folks can lighten up with a bit of wine and camaraderie?" observed Kerry.

"This was by far the most entertaining day of our trip," replied Joe. "The wine party, along with the skits and games, was great fun."

The group floated its last five miles on Day Four, which provided more surprises for the cast and crew of the wilderness troupe. Described as a "floating zoo" in one guidebook, the Rogue River had plenty of deer, bear, Chinook salmon, and steelhead, as well as numerous eagles, ospreys, and other birds to observe along the way.

Taking a lunch break after Clay Hill rapids, Joe noticed a turkey vulture munching on a dead salmon. But then a young bald eagle suddenly dropped down and stole the vulture's lunch, only to be attacked by two ospreys. The eagle dropped the fish and reluctantly acceded to the ospreys' superior numbers.

"That fish was probably the property of the ospreys to begin with," observed Paul.

"Maybe so," said Joe. "Sometimes might makes right."

Disembarking at Foster Bar, the group rendezvoused with several vans provided by the outfitter. The guides drove the river rats back to Galice, where Kerry, Paul, and Joe had a quick drink at the bar in the Galice Inn before heading out.

"This journey has been good for me, mein herring," Kerry said. "I've been pretty down since Carmina filed for divorce."

"Did you get Roxy's phone number?" Joe asked.

"Sure did," said Kerry with a broad grin. "We have a date lined up."

"Don't forget to bring the mints and condoms, mein herring," said Joe with a smirk.

CHAPTER TWENTY-FIVE

Camp Catharsis

The next summer included several wilderness expeditions. Joe made plans to visit the Strawberry Mountain Wilderness in the Prairie City Ranger District on the Malheur National Forest in Oregon for old time's sake. Excited about the trip, Joe called Kerry to see if he wanted to join him on the first of several wilderness adventures that summer.

"Herring, let's go to Prairie City," Joe suggested. "I'll show you my old stomping grounds and we can climb Strawberry Mountain."

"Man, I'd love to, mein herr," replied Kerry, "but I'm organizing what stuff I'll need to move back to Washington and getting rid of the rest. Won't be able to make this trip but looking forward to our wilderness stranger reunion later this summer in Spider Meadows with the rest of the Aldo Leopold Society. I should be situated by then."

"By the way," Kerry continued, "I contacted the Dogman, and we had a nice chat. He is, of course, looking forward to speaking with you. I caught him between Stehekin and Plain. He hoped you'd be at the Owl Compound igniting commercial-grade fireworks. Alas, he is off to Alaska's Inside Passage with his family for this vacation. But he expects to see us for our Aldo Leopold Society reunion in Spider Meadows in August."

"Okay, sounds like a plan, Mr. Vallindaklopf," said Joe. "I'll see you later in August."

"You drive a hard bargain, Hemlock," said Kerry, regurgitating a classic line from *The Eiger Sanction*.

As he drove the three hundred miles from Eugene to Prairie City to begin his quest, Joe pondered the fact that he hadn't returned to the Malheur National Forest since leaving in 1974. That first assignment had led to nearly a decade as a seasonal employee for the US Forest Service.

Joe had fond memories of roaming the wilderness south of Prairie City as a backcountry ranger. The Strawberry Mountain Wilderness is only about 69,000 acres, tiny when compared to Glacier Peak at just over 566,000 acres. The Strawberry Mountains are the southernmost range in the Blue Mountains, which extends from Walla Walla, Washington, to Burns, Oregon. The range is a unique and delightful place to explore for a summer.

Dominating the scenery at the head of the John Day River is Strawberry Mountain, elevation 9,044 feet. The wilderness itself varies between three-to-five miles in width over its eighteen-mile length, and it includes such peaks as Pine Creek Mountain, Indian Creek Butte, Strawberry Mountain, and Rabbit Ears, which range from 7,900 to over 9,000 feet.

The wilderness includes five glacial tarns, including Strawberry Lake, and the ecosystem is extremely diverse, with five of the seven North American life zones within its boundaries. The wilderness also includes thousands of acres of alpine and subalpine flora and fauna, and it features spectacular views in every direction.

Driving across Eastern Oregon, Joe realized that he had forgotten about the hot, dry, and dusty nature of the country—with sagebrush, grasslands, cows, and cowboys—as far as the eye could see. Roadside placards also reminded him of the political climate in these parts. Joe rolled his eyes as he whisked by all the signs promoting conservative candidates and ballot measures.

After a meal at The Hitchin' Post in Prairie City and a visit to see his old berth at the Forest Service bunkhouse on the compound, Joe promptly scampered up the road south to the Strawberry Campground.

Joe expected that it would be cooler at Strawberry Campground than the one-hundred-degree temperatures in John Day, and indeed it was. The next morning, Joe hit the trail to Strawberry Mountain, starting his climb at seven in the morning to beat the heat. Up the trail about a mile sits Strawberry Lake: after another mile, Strawberry Falls.

Just beyond the falls, Joe met two Lane Community College (LCC) nursing instructors. After a brief conversation, they all agreed to take each other's pictures at the summit.

The trail was both better—and worse—than he remembered. After the falls, the path became more precipitous, but the trail eventually leveled out on the ridge. After another reasonable section, the serious work began. Though the trail was clearly visible the whole way, the final pitch to the summit featured scree of all shapes and sizes, making for difficult footing.

Strawberry Lake on the trail to the summit

Joe and the LCC instructors reached the top at noon, took the requisite summit photos, then dropped back down the trail. The

LCC instructors promised Joe a cold brew back at camp to encourage an expeditious trip down the trail. They accomplished the task in three hours.

After returning to Eugene from Eastern Oregon, Joe called Kerry and invited him on a trip into the Glacier Peak Wilderness two weeks hence. Now relocated in the Seattle area, Kerry would join Joe for a return trip to Buck Creek Pass, Joe's favorite spot in the entire district.

Joe and Kerry had spent many memorable moments at Buck Creek Pass and its vicinity, so it was a natural first choice for an expedition into the Glacier Peak Wilderness that summer. Meeting at the Owl Conservatory to initiate preparations for their next adventure, Joe suddenly grew philosophical.

Joe began. "You know, herring, over the years, we have learned the symmetry between a trek down a dirt path and a journey down the road of life. We have chosen to walk this way together. Through all the ups and downs, the adverse weather, lost trails, hiccups, and uncertainties, we have persevered."

"Herring, you are waxing poetic again, just like the man of letters that you have become," replied Kerry nonchalantly. "You know, you'll be the one responsible for telling our story someday."

"Of course," responded Joe, casually absorbing Kerry's cryptic comment without a second thought.

"By the way, did you bring the mushrooms?" Kerry asked.

"I did indeed," replied Joe.

"Well, let's get started," suggested Kerry.

The two former wilderness rangers popped a few fungi, opened the first of two bottles of port, and swapped stories around the council fire until the wee hours.

Due to their late night of fun and debauchery, Joe and Kerry wouldn't make it to the trailhead at Trinity until three in the afternoon. Their organizational efforts resembled the Russian army prior to WW II: dazed and confused. Nonetheless, they would—like that same Russian army—ultimately prevail.

Their goal was to pack lightly, which required coordination. For example, no need for two camp stoves, two tents, or two sets of cookware. So, Kerry and Joe, unlike the approach they took in the old days, methodically discussed who would bring what as they planned their daily meals before leaving.

Settling on gear, Kerry and Joe trudged up the hot and dusty trail, fending off the black flies in the eighty-degree temperatures as they hiked. As the sun grew low in the sky, they passed the junction of the Buck Creek Trail and the Chiwawa Basin Trail before settling on a well-worn campsite near the footbridge over the Chiwawa River for their first overnight stop.

After setting up camp, they were relieved—after all the preparation and planning—to finally be in the wilderness. Tomorrow would be another day. And what a day it would be.

In the middle of the night, Joe awoke suddenly as the inside of his tent was illuminated by a full moon that reappeared from behind the clouds. At daybreak, the skies were clear, but a high cloud cover would soon sweep into the valley. They broke camp and continued the long trek to Buck Creek Pass, about eight more miles up the trail.

Kerry reminded Joe what Fred Beckey, the legendary mountaineer and author, said about the proliferation of unnecessary switchbacks added to the trail by the Forest Service.

"Yes, mein herring," said Joe. "I was partially responsible for that. But Fred probably doesn't give a shit about unacceptably muddy crossings from stock animals on the old trail."

"True dat," replied Kerry.

After an hour, ominous gray clouds rolled in, and the predicted storm brought rain. The good news was that the rain wiped out the black flies completely for the next twenty-four hours. More good news: the storm was brief, and the sun shortly reappeared for the remainder of the day.

By the time Joe and Kerry reached mile nine on the Buck Creek Trail, they were clearly ready to call it a day and pitch camp. As the trail rounded Helmet Butte on the north side of the pass, they were rewarded for their patience and persistence. They stared at the stunning views of Buck Mountain, Mt. Berge, and Mt. Cleator down the valley and observed Glacier Peak to the west.

Joe reminded Kerry as they gazed at the view. "You know, mein freund, Sylvester considered Buck Creek Pass to be the most beautiful spot in the entire region."

"And with good reason," replied Kerry.

The next day, they would trek even higher—back to High Pass.

Morning arrived with a clear blue sky and the sun rising above the eastern slopes, a rare occasion in the North Cascades with nary a cloud in sight. Joe knew that the bright sunrise would ignite Glacier Peak's white coat against an azure sky.

"Wake up, herring!" Joe implored Kerry. "Glacier Peak will be lit up like a lantern."

"I've seen it before, mein freund," responded Kerry, as he rolled over in his sleeping bag.

Buck Creek Pass is famed for its vistas of Glacier Peak, but only if you can see it through the ever-present cloud cover. Even in the summer, the mountain seldom reveals its summit. Maritime clouds from the west side typically tend to collect at the crest of the Cascades in the summer, so opportunities for picture-perfect views of Glacier Peak are exceedingly rare.

After hustling up the trail to a nearby promontory for a few photos, they had breakfast before preparing for their day hike to High Pass. After cleaning up, they trekked up the High Pass Trail for even more stunning mountain panoramas. With the snow having recently receded above seven thousand feet, it was springtime in August. They passed lush beds of wildflowers—including paintbrush, lupine, and western anemone—that blanketed treeless hillsides above timberline.

About halfway up the High Pass Trail, Kerry and Joe encountered impassable snowfields at the eight-thousand-foot level, so they returned to a nearby saddle where they could observe both the Buck Creek Valley and upper Suiattle River, one of the most obscure corners of the Glacier Peak Wilderness. After lunch, they headed back to explore more of Buck Creek Pass before dinner.

High Pass and Triad Lake

That night Joe prepared a meal of macaroni and cheese enlivened with fried Spam, garlic, and onions.

"You're not going to eat that shit, are you?" Kerry inquired.

"Absolutely, you'll have to give it a try," said Joe.

"Hey, this is quite good, herring," Kerry admitted after sampling a couple of bites.

A month later, the Aldo Leopold Society gathered for their much-anticipated reunion at the end of the summer. The day had finally arrived after months in the planning stages. In all, nine former wilderness strangers would hit the trail together again. For some, it would be an opportunity to purge demons—be it a relationship gone bad, the loss of a loved one, or simply the opportunity to expel the nattering nabobs of negativism in society.

But first, they congregated at Fergie's house in Leavenworth for a party. The group then planned to venture into the Glacier Peak Wilderness, this time up the Phelps Creek Trail to Spider Meadows.

Participants came from near and far to join the reunion tour: New Hope, Pennsylvania; Pioneer, California; Anchorage, Alaska; Austin, Texas; Eugene, Oregon; Boise, Idaho; Toronto, Ontario; and Seattle, Washington. For some, the journey provided the type of emotional relief that only the wilderness can provide.

The concept of wilderness as a gateway to catharsis has been "en vogue" since Biblical times, as both Moses and Jesus sought repose in the wilderness. The notion continues to retain its significance to the present day, with wilderness providing an environment of physical hardship where spiritual catharsis can occur—a place to relieve emotional baggage.

The notion centers on the belief that those who need consolation can find respite from the pressures of civilization—a sanctuary if you will—in the wilderness. And so it was, on Monday, August 17, the Aldo Leopold Society departed from the Phelps Creek Trailhead in the Glacier Peak Wilderness to seek renewal and restoration in Spider Meadows.

Considering that every individual had worked with horses, mules, and burros back in the day, it was only appropriate that the Dogman and his now-wife, Conifer A. Coil, reserved a pack string complete with the attendant wranglers to transport fresh food, along with a generous supply of wine, beer, and other accoutrements.

Departing the trailhead at ten in the morning, they enjoyed perfect weather—cool and windy enough to keep the black flies at bay, but delightfully sunny, nonetheless. Most everybody had arrived in Spider Meadows by one in the afternoon, but a downed log near the one-mile marker delayed the wranglers, who were breaking in a new mule, and their pack string.

While a few waited patiently for the arrival of the wranglers, others struck out from Spider Meadows for a quick hike to Upper Phelps Creek where, despite the excessive heat that summer, snow still stubbornly clung to the shadowed areas of the high mountain basin. The water in the creek was cold and delicious.

Back at Spider Meadows, the little tent city they had established as their base of operation was dubbed "Camp Catharsis" by one jester.

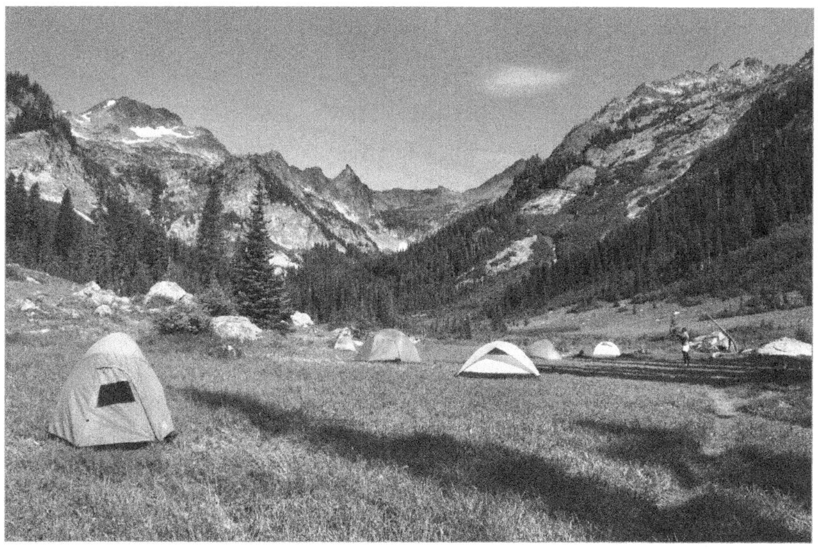

Camp Catharsis in Spider Meadows

"Truly we are living lives of leisure here, much like the landed gentry," mused the Dogman.

"You dog, speak for yourself," said Kerry. "I'm with the hoi polloi. I could use some *dinero*."

"It's just 'hoi polloi,' mein herring," countered the Dogman, using an annoyingly superior tone. "You don't need a 'the' in front of it. 'Hoi polloi' already means *the common people*."

"That's right, I forgot; we have another man of letters in our midst," Kerry replied. "Or in your case, a dog of letters."

The destination on the first full day for the group was a trip up Spider Glacier to Spider Gap, the pass that overlooks Lyman Lakes on the Chelan Ranger District on the other side. The hike would be an opportunity to reminisce and socialize while gaining elevation up to the pass.

The trail to Spider Gap is not for wimps. Miners from the Royal Development Company based at Trinity had built the trail, an outpost for the company assayer during the summer months. The steep grade fails to meet federal criteria for backcountry trails, but the Forest Service continues to maintain the popular approach to Lyman Lakes and beyond.

Leaving Spider Meadows, the trail skirts below a sheer cliff before ascending quickly through sparse greenery to Spider Glacier adjacent to the East Arm of Chiwawa Mountain. The views of Mt. Maude, Seven-Fingered Jack, Mt. Fernow, Copper Peak, Red Mountain, and Chiwawa Mountain are spectacular from the upper portion of the trail.

Three groups of Aldo Leopold Society trekkers departed camp over the course of an hour, so everybody connected either coming or going, allowing for a bit of tomfoolery and mugging for the cameras. Back in Spider Meadows, the exhilaration from the day's hike permeated camp.

Libations were in order, and soon the stories began to cascade—tales of horses bolting to the trailhead after a full day of trail work, footraces to Pass No Pass from Buck Creek Trail, total lunar eclipses, meteor showers against a jet-black wilderness sky, and encounters with deer, bear, coyotes, cougars, and survivalists.

For dinner, Joe prepared his *pièce de resistance*—macaroni and cheese with Spam, garlic, and onions.

"Spam?" asked the Dogman.

"You must trust Doctor Gonzo on this one, folks," said Kerry. "He has a unique way of cooking the meal, with sautéed onions, garlic, and, of course, Spam. Tasting Joe's epicurean delight, the doubters conceded the dish was indeed delicious.

After dinner, more wine—and more embellished tales of life in the wilderness—flowed until dark. Because of high fire danger, campfires were prohibited even in wilderness areas, so when dusk fell, the party ended. Helmut Vallindaklopf's evil twin, Ramone, made a cameo appearance briefly and grew quite amorous, but he was chased off by three strong-willed, intelligent women, including Conifer A. Coil.

The day had waned and, with a general sense of gratification from their workout, they could sleep easy that night, even on hard ground. For many, this reunion was about the opportunity to spend time reconnecting with old friends. The bonus of meeting in the wilderness was gratifying for one and all.

Morning brought a day of transition for the cathartic campers. Some would venture to Upper Phelps Creek to the base of Dumbbell Mountain, listed among the one hundred highest peaks in Washington. Dumbbell, another whimsical mountain moniker created by A.H. Sylvester, towers over the basin.

A 1926 article in *Mazama* magazine titled "In the Glacier Peak Region" described Dumbbell Mountain as "a ponderous gendarme in regal isolation and reaching to a dizzy height." The mountain was undoubtedly climbed by miners in the prospecting era.

The next day, some in the group decided to head back to the trailhead. As members of the Aldo Leopold Society said their long good-byes, the group agreed that a nearby unnamed peak at the head of the valley should be called "Cathartic Spire" in honor of their summit meeting in Spider Meadows.

As some trekked back to the trailhead, heated discussions ensued about characters from their past and nostalgic tales about their time as wilderness rangers. Near the one-mile marker on the Phelps Creek Trail, they stopped to pay their respects to Red Mountain Ole, one of the original miners in the area, who is buried next to the trail where thousands pass by without a clue.

Red Mountain Ole was one among many miners of his genre who toiled hard and braved extreme winter weather yet seldom had much to show for their efforts. A colorful character, Ole roamed the ridges of the Upper Chiwawa River area for years, trapping silver foxes, whose skins fetched more money than gold nuggets.

After the long drive down the Chiwawa River Road to Lake Wenatchee, Kerry and Joe stopped at Midway Grocery for a six-pack of Corona, then adjourned to the Owl Conservatory to celebrate their wilderness excursion. Several in the Aldo Leopold Society were already talking about "next year."

Red Mountain from Phelps Ridge

In September, Joe received a call from Kerry.

"Break out the port, mein herring," said Kerry. "It's that time of the year. I'll be coming down to Eugene for our annual trip to the Duck-Husky football game. Can you get tickets?"

"Of course, mein freund," replied Joe. "I already have them."

"Good," said Kerry. "Fix up your guest room, warm up the hot tub, and alert the neighbors, because I'll be down."

Upon his arrival, Kerry appeared more subdued than usual to Joe, especially considering his unbridled enthusiasm on their recent phone call. Joe quickly noticed Kerry was abstaining from both caffeine and alcohol.

They walked over to Autzen Stadium for the game, but by half-time, the Ducks were losing badly, so they returned to the Blanco household. The next day, Kerry drove back to his sailboat moored in the Edmonds Marina.

After Kerry had left, Joe asked Rachael, "Did Kerry seem out of sorts to you?"

"Oh, yes," came her reply. "It was as plain as the nose on my face."

A week later, Joe received a letter from his friend:

Herring, we spoke of Cathartic Spire metaphorically as a peak invoking a symbol of my recovery from my recent divorce. More than all the rest of my friends combined, you have been available, both as a true friend and an ear, and as a student of the sociological phenomenon that is Carmina.

As you know, I have really appreciated the dialogue and your support. Just this evening, I seemed to come to terms with my ordeal. I'm perhaps just as guilty for falling for Carmina hook, line, and sinker. I'm not sure there's much that is genuine about her. I could make a case for her being devious from the start. As Tina Turner asked, "What's love got to do with it?"

The road trip I just took had a hidden purpose, but my journey allowed me to "tell the whole story—the rest of the story" on your upstairs deck during happy hour. Reflecting today, my trip also feels like a milestone. After our recent conversations, more than ever, I can put the entire affair in the rearview mirror, so to speak.

It's a great feeling, coming back with fewer ghosts, with less reason to fight the past. I'll take it! So, thanks again, for being what great lifelong friends can be about. Simply listening and continuing the dialogue allows progress in my efforts to move on.

Muchas gracias, amigo. This kind of progress is a big fucking deal.

Love, Kerry

CHAPTER TWENTY-SIX

Paddling into Tomorrow

Always looking for a new challenge, Kerry joined an international goodwill expedition to cross the Bering Strait by kayak from Prince of Wales, Alaska, the westernmost point of the North American continent, to Cape Dezhnev, Russia, the easternmost point on the Asian continent, slightly south of the Arctic Circle.

The Bering Strait historically had been the focus of scientific speculation that humans theoretically migrated from Asia to the North American continent across a land bridge. Lower ocean levels in the distant past could have exposed a ridge in the vicinity, allowing humans to walk from Siberia to Alaska, thereby populating North and South America thousands of years ago.

In the mid-eighties, after Soviet leader Mikhail Gorbachev assumed power, he instituted a policy of "glasnost"—a Soviet initiative permitting open discussion of political and social issues and allowing dissemination of news and information—and "perestroika," the policy of reforming the Soviet economic and political systems.

Relations between the United States and the Soviet Union subsequently began to thaw, and goodwill exercises between the countries increased. Several teams of adventurers from the Soviet Union, Great Britain, and the United States initiated the planning of two kayak expeditions across the Bering Strait.

Kerry, who had become friends with the leaders of the American group, signed on for the mission. Once the expedition had established firm dates for the historic crossing across the Bering Strait, Kerry called Joe and left a message:

> *Herring, I have big news, but it would be best for me to have a conversation instead of just leaving a message. I am out of pocket today, so I won't be available. But I will call you tonight. I would love to talk right now. I will be in a small village in Dutch Harbor this weekend, where there are no pay phones.*
>
> *I will call tonight at 7:00 p.m. Pacific Daylight Time. Currently, I remain sleep-deprived, and after taking four different medications, I now feel like I'm splitting in two on a reef. But I need to talk with you, mein herr. A big adventure awaits. Talk to you tonight.*

Precisely at seven in the evening, Joe received Kerry's call.

"Wie gehts, mein herring?" Joe inquired.

"Sehr gut," came Kerry's reply. "I'll soon embark on the kayak quest of a lifetime, mein freund. I'm part of the 'Paddling into Tomorrow' expedition that will cross the Bering Strait from Alaska to Russia. I'll send you one of the T-shirts we had printed up. We have two teams of Americans and Brits that will cross the Bering Strait from Wales, Alaska, to Cape Dezhnev, Russia."

"Well, I guess that's better than coming from the other direction," cracked Joe.

"Funny you should say that because two teams of Russians, one using a traditional whale skin boat, will attempt the same feat paddling from the other direction," replied Kerry.

"Well, be careful, mein herring," warned Joe. "As bold and foolhardy as I may seem, you have always taken adventure to another level."

"Will do," Kerry agreed. "I'll send you a missive the day before we leave."

True to his word, right before he departed on the expedition, Kerry wrote a letter to Joe.

Mein herring:

I will depart soon on the kayaking expedition across the Bering Strait. We have been training for several months now, and we depart tomorrow. Should I survive the experience, I shall have quite a story to tell.

If I do not return, for whatever reason, you need to know a few things about me. I must explain myself and this is as much for me as it is for you. Let's start with the omnipresent shadow of doom in my life's experience. I wanted to make this letter short and sweet, but after far too many attempts and drafts, this will have to do.

I have been studying my ailment, a lifelong condition that I have been saddled with since my youth. It's called persistent depressive disorder, also called dysthymia (dis-THIE-me-uh), and it is a chronic form of depression.

Those who suffer from this condition may lose interest in normal daily activities, feel hopeless, lack productivity, and have low self-esteem and an overall feeling of inadequacy. These feelings last for years and may significantly interfere with relationships, school, work, and daily activities.

This has been the story of my life, likely due to genetics, my childhood, and who knows what else. Toss in that every decade or so I experience a severe, major episode lasting as long as a year. William Styron in Darkness Visible *and David Guterson in* Descent: A Memoir of Madness *have documented the experience of suffering from dysthymia, as has David Foster Wallace.*

During these episodes of severe depression, I live with the constant kind of anxiety and fear that you see in scenes from horror movies as the music builds just before some unspeakable demon appears. Each minute of this fearsome feeling is like lying on a shallow reef offshore with a broken back as the tide rolls in.

Over the past several months, I have descended into this state of madness once again. Here is what I feel is different this time. After my last severe, major episode, I barely survived. I knew that if this happened again, it would likely kill me. When you have severe episodes, the chances of a recurrence—and of the condition becoming worse and lasting longer—are 90 percent, or 100 percent in my case.

Whether I've functioned at high levels or been brought to my knees by major severe depressive episodes, nearly all my behavior lives under this shadow. Whether working with great productivity, leading outdoor expeditions, marrying women I've loved, managing environmental mitigation projects, earning six-figure salaries for major corporations, or simply creating good outcomes for others, I ultimately fail.

My path always leads to sabotage, fleeing, and destroying everything I've created. I am my own Sherman's March, laying waste to my environment.

A few years ago, I spent a full twelve months in Dante's hell before I rallied for one more, high-functioning run, which I blew apart after we built Das Tree Haus. I managed to remain on a relatively even keel, until recently, when I've found myself in hell again.

But even my last run, when I created a lifestyle that was totally enviable, with a wife, career, home, family, pets, incredible travel, and adventures galore, was fraught with my risky behavior, which jeopardized and destroyed all I had achieved. The risky behavior included drinking every evening and withholding affection instead of tending to my best interests and needs.

I've sought medical and psychiatric help during the last three severe episodes. My experience has been that meeting with a psychiatrist for an hour once every two weeks for $200 a visit does absolutely nothing. We all know it's about trying scripts, or antidepressants. I remember that of all the medications I've tried—more than six or seven—none help. Some make me worse.

I've experienced months with little sleep, even on medications meant to induce sleep, like Ambien.

Even with medication, nightmares with foreboding circumstances make for restive sleep. I can only describe these episodes as I alluded to earlier, when an unimaginable beast is about to eviscerate a human. Recently, I've been living every minute of every day—and often night—with panic, anxiety, and fear.

I've been on 60 milligrams of Cymbalta daily for over ten years. That was the medication I was using when I walked out of the last major episode. Did it help me? Perhaps. But like Guterson and Styron have documented, I also have survived prior episodes of depression without knowing if my medications helped. So, my condition seems to have come and gone, maybe on its own.

What I have done with my life includes hundreds of glorious experiences and wilderness travel with multitudes of wonderful friends. These trips into the backcountry have always provided meaning, spirit, accomplishment, and companionship. Manic? Perhaps.

But that is what has been my focus; it's what I do: mountaineering, skiing, marathon skate skiing, long-distance cycling, plus thousands of miles of backpacking, floating and paddling wild rivers, and more recently, sailing on the high seas.

I've taken trips to Nepal, Tahiti, Europe, Mexico, Canada, and Alaska, and throughout the Pacific Northwest. Bursts of the good life, eh? The finest travel, food, wine, and interesting people. Kayaking the Grand Canyon and other rivers and hiking among the world's tallest peaks. Sailing Alaska's Inside Passage.

By comparison, I simply cannot fathom playing board games, eating in a cafeteria, watching television, doing physical therapy, or whatever comes with old age while waiting for the Grim Reaper.

Here is the essence of what I've always found missing and what I've actively repelled when provided with the choice: Love. Family. Community. Support of and by others. Home. Satisfaction. Comfort. Compromise. Meaningful enterprise.

I've had many opportunities to build a great life and live accordingly. But when faced with making the right choices, I am constricted by an unbroken forged chain, somehow forbidden from moving in a positive direction, and I literally drop off the map. I eventually find myself painted into a corner of extreme regret and remorse. I've come to accept the fact that I will inevitably throw it all away.

I trigger myself, autoimmune to life, and descend into a state of madness once again. Perhaps I've tried as hard as I could and just don't have what it takes, or so it seems at times like this. Perhaps I have just never learned how to let love in.

I'm there again—right now. The overwhelmingly enormous shadow is back. I'm nearly homeless. I've built a tree house in the mountains and refurbished a sailboat for excursions on the ocean. Sounds dreamy to many, but for me, both dwellings are tombs.

Now the depressive and forsaken episodes color everything, and I wander aimlessly like a rudderless boat. Seek medical help once again? I feel hopelessly and desperately alone. I can't even seek medical help without daily support from others—in a warm home with loving kindness.

Take a new drug after waiting a month or two for an appointment? Take a script, then wait to see if it works while I'm curled in the fetal position alone in the tree house or on my unfinished sailboat? I know my condition has never really gone away and will come back even worse.

I have no place to go, no place to be. I need to feel safe, supported, and loved while trying new pharmaceuticals from trusted providers. I am so existentially alone and bereft. This is not a cry for help. I've done that.

Each time, I've triumphantly walked out the other side and prospered once again. Then, without fail, I throw it all away. My great and enviable position in life seems just fine until I arrive in this dreadful condition once more. But given the nature of my illness, it's probably not entirely my fault.

My attitude is itself colored by depression. One can conceivably forgive oneself and reconcile this cognitively and live on. I don't appear to have the right tools in my tool chest. I've never cultivated what I need to overcome myself and find homeostasis for a happy, balanced life. When it comes to sustaining what I have built—with work, relationships, homes, and others—I crash and burn.

I only want the pain to stop. My body is beyond exhaustion. My heart has no feeling except for stone-cold fearful remorse. What did I do to deserve this?

But now, I will make one more effort to shake the madness and bounce back as I have many times before. This expedition by kayak across the Bering Strait with my colleagues from Alaska and Great Britain will be the beginning of my revival. Perhaps I will eat fresh whale, or muktuk, with Eskimos under the northern lights once again.

After this trip, I'm planning to take a cruise ship expedition to kayak and ski in Antarctica, something I've always wanted to do. Perhaps, with time, I will pull through once again. And perhaps a new episode will begin with the journey that's been dubbed "Paddling into Tomorrow."

Love, Kerry.

That would be Joe's last missive from Kerry. As Joe pondered Kerry's revelations, he had several epiphanies of his own concerning his kindred companion.

While Kerry appeared to lead a charmed life, he was incredibly lucky. But it wasn't just that he had extraordinary luck; Kerry simply didn't perceive obstacles the way most people might. He was immune to doubts, such as "Oh, I don't have the qualifications, they wouldn't hire me" or "How can I build a treehouse when I don't have any land and not much money?"

Kerry had the remarkable ability to visualize something and make it happen—design a new type of sea kayak, build a tree-house in the mountains, plan and execute fabulous trips around the world, and convince potential employers that he was the best person for the job.

Joe also understood that Kerry's sensitivity to the world around him was uniquely surreal. Kerry could sense things that others could not. Kerry was perhaps the single most visionary and loving person Joe had ever met.

From the beginning, Joe knew that Kerry was manic. Yet while they were immediately attracted to one another as kindred spirits and soul mates, they were strangers for many years.

Joe would learn that his beloved friend was manic about many things—life, adventure, the ability to create, to learn, to talk—and he was especially manic about love. He recognized that Kerry's soul was one that burned brightly, and Joe was attracted to its incandescence.

The next week, Joe was horrified to read a United Press International wire story in the (Eugene) *Register-Guard* with the headline: "Bering Strait Kayakers Rescued."

> "ANCHORAGE, Alaska—Kayakers making an historic crossing of the Bering Strait ran into trouble and had to be rescued by an Inuit Eskimo whaling vessel. Only one person, Kerry Jon Weiss, was reported missing and presumed dead, expedition members said Wednesday.
>
> 'We were too busy to be scared,' said Doug Noon, a Juneau lawyer who was one of the kayakers rescued.
>
> The expedition included four Britons in single kayaks; six Alaskans in single kayaks and a double kayak; and two brothers from California and a Hawaiian—one a paraple-

gic—paddling in a unique three-seat baidarka once used by Alaskan coastal Aleuts. The group paddled across the strait when poor weather conditions forced them to abandon their crossing and call for help.

'The weather turned on us,' said expedition member Darlene Hensel, a Fairbanks teacher. 'The fog rolled in, and waves were cresting at 40 feet. At that point, the paddlers in the baidarka subsequently made the decision to call for rescue by radioing a mayday and setting off flares.'

'Traditionally, when a rescue call is sent to the Coast Guard, all vessels and people are rescued,' said Hensel. 'An experienced kayaker like Kerry would have been aware of this fact. Thinking he could paddle to Little Diomede, he bolted in a different direction, making it difficult to locate him.'

The kayakers were seeking to paddle their way into the history books with the unprecedented trip across the Bering Strait between the United States and the Soviet Union.

The American 'Paddling into Tomorrow' team and the British 'Kayaks across the Bering Strait' team left Nome, Alaska in early June.

Paddling through ice-clogged waters up the Alaskan coastline to Wales, the closest town between the American mainland and the Soviet mainland 56 miles away, the two groups were then joined by the baidarka expedition.

When foggy weather cleared late Sunday, the combined parties left Wales for Little Diomede, halfway across the Bering Strait and a mere two miles from the Soviet island of Big Diomede. However, five hours later, the fog returned and with it came high winds and waves.

'After 13 hours of continuous paddling, the kayakers saw that the fog had lifted long enough for them to learn that they were eight miles off course, north of the Diomedes, and making little progress against the strong wind,' Hensel said.

Early Monday morning, wet and cold weather conditions were taking their toll, with one kayaker showing signs of hypothermia. They subsequently called for help.

An Eskimo boat launched from Little Diomede rescued the kayakers, hoisted some of their boats aboard, and transported them to Big Diomede, a Soviet military post. Further searches by the Soviet navy were unable to locate Weiss.

CHAPTER TWENTY-SEVEN

Too Alone at Sea

A year after Kerry went missing on the Paddling into Tomorrow expedition, an Inuit Eskimo in Point Barrow, Alaska, found his kayak nearly five hundred miles from where he was last seen near Little Diomede Island in the Bering Strait.

A few months later, Kerry's friend Rick Oldman, pursuing a tip from a fellow kayaker, surprisingly located the boat in Vancouver, British Columbia and acted on the information. Once he had the boat back home in Spokane, Rick called Joe to let him know of his discovery.

Rick began. "Joe, you'd better sit down. I have astonishing news. I learned that someone had identified a boat found on the North Slope as Kerry's. I received a tip from one of Kerry's mates on the Paddling into Tomorrow expedition that his kayak had since made its way to Vancouver."

"Wow, are you sure it's Kerry's boat?!" replied Joe.

"Yes, so I packed my bag and hitchhiked to Whistler." Rick continued, "A guy picked me up in Penticton. On the drive, I started sharing the story about Kerry and his expedition across the Bering Strait and mentioned that someone had recently found his kayak. I was in luck because the guy had not only heard the story but also knew the person who had Kerry's kayak."

"How weird is that?" replied Joe.

"Frankly, it's astonishing," continued Rick. "The guy who picked me up even gave me a ride to a job site where the fellow who had located the boat was working as a building contractor. When I started asking the contractor about the kayak, I sensed he wanted to keep the boat."

"And...?" asked Joe.

"I just assertively asked," said Rick, "'Where's the kayak? It belongs to my friend.'"

"From that point," Rick continued, "he cooperated and allowed me to take the boat back to Washington. Kerry's gear was gone, but inside the kayak, a folded-up sheet of paper was securely taped inside the vessel's map compartment. Once I was able to pry it loose, I could hardly believe what it said."

"Do you have the note?" asked Joe.

"Yes, and it's brief, but it reads like it was prepared ahead of time," replied Rick, "Here's what it said."

I'm sorry. I have reached for the magic many times and was sustained now and then. I couldn't seem to do enough for myself to make a viable difference. I feel that I carry too much mental baggage that I can't seem to shake.

Bless some of the best friends in the world for their friendship, love, and kindness, but at some point, I will succumb to a mental illness that haunts and discolors my existence. My condition removes all pleasure. My life is very deeply painful. I had hoped to slide into home base with a martini in my hand and a smile on my face. But now I believe that is too rare of a notion.

I hate 24/7 madness and I'm trapped there once again. Believe me, please, when I say that I have wished for a viable way out but have been unsuccessful with my meager efforts. I'm exhausted. To all the good times!

kjw

Six months after recovering Kerry's kayak, his family and friends held a memorial at Alki Beach in West Seattle to honor his life and legacy. His social circle was quite a diverse universe of friends. Few knew one another, though some had met at the ceremony when Kerry married Ashleigh in Leavenworth.

They all, however, held a special place in Kerry's heart at one time or another in their lives. The event included a potluck on the beach around a campfire, followed by a procession of tributes to honor Kerry.

After the potluck, Joe announced to those assembled that because Kerry's sister, Madeline Kathryn Parish, would be unable to attend his celebration of life, she had asked him to read her pre-prepared address at the beginning of the tributes to Kerry.

Joe began. "I will begin today's tribute by reading a message from Kerry's beloved sister Madeline."

Dear family and friends of Kerry Jon Weiss, you are all beloved individuals who knew and loved Kerry.

I want to thank you personally for taking the time from your busy schedules to pay such a lovely tribute to my dear brother, who I can still recall pushing in a stroller as a toddler. He was so very fortunate to have all of you in his life at the various times and places that he did. Each and every one of you meant different things to Kerry at different times in his life.

And he enjoyed each and every one of you on one adventure or another. His life was enriched by all of you, and he never hesitated to share these stories with me. Some of you I know personally and others I know through his stories. But you were all friends, and for that, I thank you now and forever.

As you honor Kerry today, I want you to realize what you mean to me personally for having shared in Kerry's life. Because of all of you, it was what it was and what a life it was! He was much more than a brother to me. Other than my beautiful husband, whom I lost just a year previously, Kerry was my dearest friend. I shall miss him every day of my life but hope to stay connected to you through letters and phone calls.

God bless each and every one of you. As you head into the wilderness, carry the memory of Kerry with you. Somehow, he will know he is on another adventure with you, and he will remain with us forever.

Happy trails, friends. Sister Madeline Kathryn Parish

After Joe had read Madeline's homage to Kerry, a procession of friends read their individual tributes. Once those in attendance had the opportunity to speak, Joe proceeded with his own eulogy paying homage to Kieran Jon Weiss:

Herr Vallidaklopf:

What are the chances? Sight unseen, two people eventually connect because another person said, "you've gotta meet this guy" to each of us? It must have been destiny. Nay, it was unavoidably inevitable, my friend.

Seeing your face pressed against the glass on the front window of the Mushroom Haus is how my life with you began. Right away, I loved your adventurous spirit. You were bold, daring, brave, and, at times, you threw caution to the wind.

I figured you would eventually leave this planet after a fatal encounter with a polar bear—or an orca. Instead, you fell victim to a more formidable beast: depression. As I and many here today would attest, we are undeniably and understandably sad you are not here with us.

We are all very thankful we even had the opportunity—and privilege—to bask in your luminance. Your spirit attracted many circles of friends, all unique solar systems in a galaxy of friendships.

We will miss you very much, but we will carry your spirit forward in new wilderness adventures. We will always remember our wondrous days together with you.

So, here's an overview of our lives together in a nutshell.

Terrorizing other wilderness rangers on the bar circuit at the fire prevention training in Ellensburg. Guzzling strawberry daiquiris at the Mushroom Haus. Hanging with Krazy Ken and the Flying Swatzahili Sisters in your apartment in the Tannebaum Building in Leavenworth.

Bushwhacking up the Napeequa River with Raoul in a primeval forest to burn down a squatter's cabin. Trudging up the Chiwawa River on our daily visits to Chickamin Creek to labor on the world's longest ditch. Paddling up the Entiat River from our home base on the mighty Columbia.

Rushing the stage at a Dire Straits concert after crashing a cocktail party at the Crowne Plaza. Yes, we had many, many stories to share around the campfire.

Now, a bit of wordplay: Spiderman. Paul's 'banana' bread. Which mountain? Range 700: maximum firepower. Raoooul! Pancake. Das Cabin. Go Ducks. Buddy, sweetheart, pal. Port season. Freitag, you asshole! Owl Conservatory. Salmon-head surprise. Pav's. Tales of Tater Boy.

Toward the end, you knew that you were living your dream, yet you were also acutely aware that your journey was no prolonged vacation. You understood that your life was a choice, just like any other, with advantages and disadvantages. You sacrificed some things for others. You knew, as poet Philip Larkin lamented: "Things are tougher than we are."

As we say good-bye, my friend, we will remember the good times: your incendiary energy, engaging personality, wild spirit, keen intelligence, innate curiosity, abundant generosity, and loving kindness. Like Leo Tolstoy, you wanted movement and not a calm course of existence. You wanted excitement and danger and the chance to sacrifice yourself for love.

Yes, you loved. And I assure you, my friend, you were loved by many in return, including all who have gathered today. Auf wiedersehen, mein herring. I will see you on the other side of the pass.

Afterword

"Kerry" was a true friend of mine, maybe my best friend. He was a hiking and drinking and traveling and cabin-building companion. We all lived vicariously through Kerry's many adventures.

Like many of our fellow wilderness rangers, I thought Kerry had everything any man might ever hope for: wilderness, women, wild adventures, stimulating careers. But we were wrong. He had given up hope. He had given up on life. And we all missed the signs.

Kerry suffered from dysthymia, a specific type of prolonged and protracted depression. I had never really thought of him as other than an always happy and enthusiastic lover of life. But, like too many Americans, Kerry had suffered long bouts of deep depression throughout his life going back to his youth.

According to the Anxiety and Depression Association of America:

- Over 264 million people worldwide live with depression.
- In 2017, around 17.3 million adults ages eighteen or older in the US had experienced at least one major depressive episode in the last year (6.7 percent of adults in the US).
- Anxiety disorders are the most common mental illness in the US, affecting 40 million adults in the United States ages eighteen and older, or 18.1 percent of the population every year.
- Anxiety disorders are highly treatable, yet only 36.9 percent of those suffering receive treatment.

Numerous prominent American authors have detailed their personal battles with depression: Andrew Solomon, William Styron, David Guterson, David Foster Wallace, Anne Sexton, Rick Moody, and many more. An entire genre of novels details the lives of people suffering from various kinds of mental illness.

And yet, as Styron especially points out in his powerful book, *Darkness Visible*, victims of mental health illness (and their friends or relatives) too often try to deny their condition, no matter how obvious their symptoms might seem, preferring to avoid facing the truth.

Kerry is far from alone in his illness. According to the American Foundation for Suicide Prevention, in 2020, there were approximately 1.2 million suicide attempts; about 45,000 Americans died by suicide; suicide is the twelfth leading cause of death in the United States.

If you are suffering from depression, anxiety, or mood swings, or if you know someone who is, please know that there are many avenues for help, starting with the National Institute of Mental Health (NIMH) and continuing with numerous state and local centers, mental health professionals, and support agencies that are available everywhere to everyone. Help is available.

From the NIMH website:

> *If you know someone in crisis: Call the National Suicide Prevention Lifeline at 1-800-273-TALK (8255) or website at https://suicidepreventionlifeline.org, or text the Crisis Test Line (https://www.crisistextline.org) or text HELLO to 741741. Both services are free and available 24 hours a day, seven days a week. All calls are confidential. Contact social media outlets directly if you are concerned about a friend's social media updates or dial 911 in an emergency. Learn more on the Lifeline website (https://suicidepreventionlifeline.org) or the Crisis Text Line's website at https://www.crisistextline.org.*

As of July 2022, the National Suicide Prevention Lifeline—the number posted on student identification cards, atop Google search results, and in warning labels on television shows—has become 988, casting it as the 911 for mental health.

Operators will have the ability to counsel callers and dispatch specially trained responders, reducing interventions by armed law enforcement and reliance on emergency rooms.

J.C.M.

Made in the USA
Las Vegas, NV
09 November 2022

59055459R00134